DISCARDED

D1530612

Religion May Be
Hazardous to Your Health

Religion May Be Hazardous

to Your Health

by
ELI S. CHESEN, M.D.

Peter H. Wyden, Inc. / *Publisher*
New York

LEARNING RESOURCE CENTER
OCEAN COUNTY ... TO 'S RIVER. N. J.

155.9
C524r

RELIGION MAY BE HAZARDOUS TO YOUR HEALTH

COPYRIGHT © 1972 BY ELI S. CHESEN

All rights reserved, including the right to reproduce
this book, or parts thereof, in any form, except for
the inclusion of brief quotations in a review.

Names and identifying details
of all persons in all case histories have
been altered to safeguard their privacy.

Library of Congress Catalog Card Number: 76-189524

MANUFACTURED IN THE UNITED STATES OF AMERICA

TO MY DAUGHTER

CHELSEA LYNN

45665

45865

Acknowledgments

I would like to extend special gratitude to Margaret M. Klinkroth for her library research and to my wife, Peggy, for her aid in preparation of this manuscript. I am also grateful to Mr. Richard C. Danielson for his inspiration on this subject many years ago and to Mr. Barry M. Price for his tenacious encouragement.

Contents

Religion May Be
Hazardous to Your Health

Introduction: How This Book Can Help Your Mental Health

Religion is actually a kind of consumer good that is without question potentially harmful to the user's mental health.

One must be impressed by the zealous concern of today's consumer for what he consumes. There has been a veritable renaissance of such interest in light of the current realization that many products do not live up to their names and claims. But it is not yet widely recognized that religion, like many of these products, also can be useless and even dangerous, at least from a psychiatric point of view.

I intend to approach religion as though it were simply a commodity; when "purchased" by the consumer, it is capable of benefiting as well as harming him. I am concerned, therefore, with the effects that religion can be shown to have on mental health as well as on mental illness.

I am not espousing atheism or any other religious stance. I am merely setting down a series of conclusions based upon the observations of case histories that are representative of literally thousands of others. The paraphrased histories that are incorporated into this book are not unusual or seldom-seen cases of special or rare academic interest. They are, rather, typical of cases seen every day in the offices of privately practicing psychiatrists and on the wards of most mental health facilities.

The range of emotional difficulty in these patients varies from the existence of subtle disturbances to major ones in which at times the person does not know who he is but, rather, thinks that he is Jesus Christ, the Virgin Mary, or God. In each instance I intend to demonstrate how tenacious religious beliefs can be an active thread interwoven into the tapestry of a disturbed thinking process.

In developing this theme, I shall set out a series of axioms that, though difficult to prove "beyond any semblance of doubt," nevertheless lend themselves to convincing documentation. The early chapters deal with examples of religious interplay in the developing child and adolescent. Later chapters delve deeper: they deal with the part that religion often seems to play in the evanescence of one's reality and consequent plunge into mental illness.

I will also discuss some disastrous consequences of newly founded radical religious movements, such as the "Jesus Freaks" and others that flourish among those who have adopted the "hippie" life style. Here the misuse of religion brings on particularly devastating results.

I will approach the problems that arise from religion's attitude toward unwanted pregnancy, population control, and other life situations. This will be followed by a discussion of the opposite side of the coin: those aspects of religion that serve to promote mental health.

Finally, I present a guide for parents so they can help their children to develop a healthy attitude toward religion. The reader might inquire how I reconcile these final chapters with the title of this book. My paraphrasing of the Surgeon General's cigarette-pack warning was deliberate;

religion, like cigarettes, *may* be harmful to the user's health. But unlike cigarettes, religion can also be shown to enhance one's well-being. It is time for the consumer of religion to know how.

1

Some Ground Rules

I would like first to justify the metaphor that religion is a kind of consumer good.

Like goods, religion is something that the public is constantly buying and selling to each other. It is available in a myriad of forms and can be purchased for a variety of prices. Some church memberships imply status; in this sense they are similar to country clubs and, like country clubs, have very exclusive congregations. Other memberships are more economical and therefore have less exclusive but often more enthusiastic followings.

In the selling of religion, highly complex sales campaigns permeate all the media on a national level. On the local level individual parishes act as small franchises backed by an internationally established chain organization. Though the "primary" aim of the organization is to sell the product, large assets provide a secondary gain that can be so great that it rivals our biggest corporations'.

A singular peculiarity sets religion apart from other "goods": it generally possesses an effective immunity from deserved criticism and therefore is not controlled like other goods by the usual checks and balances. Religion does not have to compete against anything in order to survive its built-in pitfalls. It is something sacred and therefore usually accepted with few questions on the part of the buyer. It is a familial legacy passed on from parent to child in a way similar to many biologically inherited characteristics. This parental passage meets very little resistance in its assimilation by young impressionable minds—minds that cannot yet think independently in the adult sense of the word.

When referring to religion in this book, I define it in its most popular sense, which need not coincide exactly with definitions popularized by the clergy. Nor does this definition necessarily conform exactly to those concepts created by the initial charters of any given religion. Rather, I refer to the laity and their own religious concepts, which may to some extent be distortions of religious actuality. I am justified in doing this because it will become apparent that it is a person's own interpretation of his religion that interplays with other aspects of his life. A multitude of would-be criticisms raised by the clergy are therefore absolutely invalid.

From the case histories it will be evident that the degree of literalism and intensity with which people indulge their religions is infinite. Unfortunately, it would be belated to say in rebuttal of these histories that the patient merely misunderstood his religion or overemphasized it. It is therefore not the clergy's preachment but the patient's interpretation of that preachment that is of concern.

I am also concerned with further distortions of religion occurring when a parent reinterprets it for his offspring. Though such distorted concepts may resemble the original beliefs only slightly, they nevertheless continue to be someone's idea of religion. And while a particular religious practice may be beneficial or harmless when unaltered, it may take on a new and destructive meaning in the hands of a parent bent on using it as a means to his own end.

I do not claim expertise in pure theology; this is not a requisite to the study of religion as an etiology. Just as many diseases of unknown cause are today often successfully studied, so do I approach the study of religion from the vantage point of its aftereffects. In other words, I am more concerned with what religion does than with what it is. I am hopeful that this redefinition and its implications will serve as a report to the consumer on some of the possible hazards that may be associated with his practice of religion.

2

Religion and Child Development

Axiom 1: Religion serves in many ways to impede the development of flexible thinking processes. This ultimately results in adult thinking that is rigid, confined and stereotyped.

A multitude of influences, some subtle, others obvious, shape an individual's personality from birth through adolescence. Whether directly, through didactic classroom lecturing and churchgoing, or indirectly, by assimilation of parental attitudes, religion is one of these influences.

As the child ascends through his childhood and adolescence he will acquire knowledge only in the context of his previous experiences and prejudices. For example, by the time a child reaches the age of five, his learning in school is already a modified process; it is affected by what he already has learned at home and elsewhere. He will, even at that age, tend to prejudge the material to be learned, the friends to be made, and the teachers to whom he is exposed.

For example, a black child's attitude toward his white schoolteacher will be very different from the attitude of his white classmates. This is not simply because he is black but rather because he has already absorbed ideas and attitudes from his parents regarding white people. The religious attitudes of the young similarly affect the mode by which he will approach and accept fresh learning material and life experiences.

How, then, does religion influence the child as he attempts to master everything from reading, writing, and arithmetic to biology, physics, and philosophy? More important, how does religion affect a child's approach to life in general?

Despite outcries by many members of the clergy that religion, philosophy, and the sciences ultimately reconcile one another, one need not search hard to find pathetic exceptions. The contrast between a child's religious background and his approach to new learning material provides a real conflict.

Consider the story of Adam and Eve. Reinterpretation of this Biblical tale, in light of Darwinian theory, becomes a cumbersome and extraordinarily futile task. The first chapter of Genesis states that God created the sun, moon, stars, day, and night on the fourth day; fish and birds on the fifth day. It goes on to say that terrestrial animals and man were created on the next day.

Yet since Charles Darwin wrote *The Origin of Species* and *The Descent of Man*, it has become universally accepted that man was created not as a unique entity, but evolved in a process taking hundreds of centuries. Darwin died in 1882; today, almost a century later, children are still being taught the fairy-tale concept that man was created on the sixth day. In the wake of Darwin's direct Biblical confrontation, it was not surprising that clergymen vigorously fought against the teaching of evolutionary theory.

Modern Bible scholars might counter this example by

defending it as something symbolic and therefore not to be construed literally. Nevertheless, the *literal* explanation is the one fixed in the child's mind until challenged by new information. While proceeding through life, the child with a sound Biblical background must then continually revise, reinterpret, and/or cast off old ideas before he can accept the new ones.

For example, Richard, age five, becomes acquainted with the Book of Genesis; when Richard is twelve, his science teacher gives a lecture on "natural selection" and evolutionary theory. The boy *is* able to grasp these new theories, but he must simultaneously deal with what Genesis told him seven years earlier. This is analogous to the way the Catholic Church has historically had to revise, reinterpret, and cast off old ideas because of scientific discovery and popular demand. The conflict could have been avoided by deleting the creation story from five-year-old Richard's Sunday School curriculum.

Another conflict arises when a child of a particular religious faith encounters peers of dissimilar faiths. In a world of literally hundreds of religions it becomes obvious, even to the naïve child, that some or all of these dogmatisms must be wrong. The child must then draw one of several conclusions:

1. All religions must be invalid.
   (This represents a rebellious kind of conflict, or atheistic reaction.)
2. Certain religions are valid only for certain people.
   (This depicts a compromise.)
3. All religions are invalid except mine.
   (This symbolizes the most self-centered, or egocentric, resolution of the multiple-religion conflict.)

The last, rather narrow-minded assumption, unfortunately holds firmly in the minds of many children and adults, though to a varying degree. Generally, the more fundamental and assertive a religion seems to be, the more often this assumption is upheld. This rather artificial and potentially harmful mode of thinking is fostered by egotistic parents, clergymen, Sunday School teachers, and television programs.

If a child could somehow be isolated from "womb to tomb" within an environment containing only one kind of religious exposure, he would perhaps not be adversely affected. Unfortunately, such homogeneity does not exist, and so children invariably proceed through their development needing constantly to interpret their religions against a backdrop of other persuasions.

Such a self-centered interpretation serves to rationalize the exclusion of those facets of other religions that are not compatible with one's own beliefs. This in turn presents to the growing child a tremendous conflict, which can be dealt with only through the three resolutions I have already mentioned. The magnitude of this conflict is perhaps best illustrated by closer examination of the two more extreme resolutions (1 and 3).

In resolution 1 the child who is confronted with several religions, including of course his own, decides that all religion must be invalid. This complete rejection of all religion usually occurs in the older child or adolescent. It may take the common form of a college freshman's religious rebellion, manifested by a nuance of self-styled atheistic ideology. The new philosophy, as far as he is concerned, is a culmination of "new" ideas resulting from meeting and listening to professors and college peers. This rebellion is needlessly perplexing to his parents, who suddenly come to the realization that they have reared a "village atheist." Despite what the young neophilosopher infers as the reason for his new-found thinking, it really represents a last, but unnecessary, stage of his adolescent rebellion. It is like a convulsant reaction to his parents and their rigid teachings.

This rejection of parental religious influences can occur automatically as a result of the sudden awareness of inconsistencies between religion and reality. Incidentally, this is happening at a time when a child is, classically, wrestling with and trying to get a grasp on reality. If he has been brought up with an unusually strong religious faith, he may now feel uneasy reconciling beliefs previously taken for granted.

The rejection occurs at this point because the child is becoming more sophisticated, and his feeling of discomfort stimulates him to seek a way to neutralize the now recognizable religion-actuality conflict. His extreme atheistic stance becomes a convenient way to forget the many inconsistencies between his religion and actuality. The consequences of such reactive thinking tend to do two things for the child:

1. Form a greater cleavage between his parents and him.
2. Strip him entirely of religion.

The undesirability of the first consequence is evident; the drawback of the second is no less conspicuous. Religion in some forms can be an asset to a child in these turbulent years of life. Finding himself stripped completely of it can contribute to general feelings of insecurity and to pseudoarrogance. Had religion been introduced to him in a more palatable and less concentrated form, he might have avoided becoming an adolescent atheist.

It is an interesting sidelight that these adolescents usually take pride in their atheism and enjoy vocalizing about it in a semi-intellectual fashion. This serves as an effective cover-up for the unsure feelings that probably always accompany this denial of God and religion. I would add that this rebellion or reaction is not always a transient one peculiar to adolescents; it is observable at cocktail parties, where immature young to middle-age adults are often preoccupied with enthusiastic colloquies about atheism. Perhaps this is representative of a person's failure to complete his adolescent rebellion.

Resolution 2 (certain religions are valid for certain people) is the easiest for a child to tolerate. The thought that a given religion is particularly valid for a given person is, to me, somewhat naïve. This "compromise," however, is the easiest for a child to adhere to because it does not force him to defend and compare various beliefs.

In resolution 3 the child confronts the myriad religions by concluding that all religions are invalid except his own. With his rejection of all foreign religion, there is a concomitant plunge into the depths of his own religion. This fosters a rigidity that precludes objective thinking much of the time. With strong childhood acceptance of religious gospel comes an inflexibility or perversion in the perception of what he sees and hears. It is this alteration of environmental interpretation that inhibits open-minded learning.

I refer again to the Book of Genesis and its teaching that God "created" the heaven and the earth. This vague conception of creation may be taught, for example, to a six-year-old and be retained by him indefinitely. Let us assume that this person has a profound religious faith and later becomes interested in geology and geophysics. These fields of science are intimately concerned with a variety of earth-creation theories. As our subject attempts to study such theory, he may find difficulty in being objective. His naïve and archaic Biblical ideas stand between him and his scientific judgment. If his Biblical influence is especially tenacious, our friend may find it necessary to change his chosen field of interest.

A child reads, listens, observes, and generally perceives through a kind of polarized filter that stifles objective observation and negates flexible, innovative, and creative thinking. What I describe here obviously is a phenomenon that occurs in variable degrees within various people. At one end of the spectrum are children who are essentially indifferent to religious dogma and who therefore are not vulnerable to what I call the "filter effect"; at the other extreme are those children who, from a very early age, are fed a kind of religious concentrate.

If their exposure to religion in this concentrated form has been intense enough and introduced at an early enough age, they may well be assuming a personal handicap that will manifest itself at a later age. If later in the life of this handicapped child other conditions become unfavorable, the results will be catastrophic. The result may in fact be a profound mental illness requiring long-term treatment. I will show later that religion is often an essential ingredient in evolving mental illness.

As the filter effect contributes to inflexible thinking, another associated mechanism comes into play. This other mechanism is an offshoot of religious indoctrination and acts as a protector of the indoctrinated material. As the child of religion grows up he assimilates into his thought processes a religious "fail-safe"—a self-protection mechanism. The fail-safe—unfortunately an implicit byproduct of almost every religion—serves to protect the person from any "alien" experiences or ideas that might be incompatible with his already inflexible way of thinking. This mechanism is a very necessary component of the rigid thinker's mind: without it he is vulnerable to new concepts, and these might threaten his stereotyped way of thinking and upset his dogmatic applecart.

As an example, how does today's devout Catholic rationalize his right to have ten children in a world threatened by overpopulation? How is he able to do this in spite of the general awareness of the apparent adverse consequences?

The answer to these questions lies in the anatomy of his thinking processes. He is protected by his fail-safe from the surrounding general awareness and can in fact avoid and shut out consideration of the conflict altogether, simply because *he "knows" that he is right and that everyone else is wrong*. His "faith" tells him so. He has known this throughout his life and is therefore impervious to the thought that he might be incorrect. This is his fail-safe.

During the past several years I have engaged in many debates with friends over matters of ecological and sociological significance. In many instances my friendly opponent was of the Catholic faith and because of this would advocate a position opposite to mine on matters of contraception, divorce, and other issues. I was always more intrigued by the Catholic *method* of argumentation than by the actual position taken in an argument. The latter was quite predictable because Church positions on these matters seem to be well delineated. The methodology of Catholic argumentation is often quite disturbing.

I have found that logic and consideration are often replaced by dogmatic or reflexive testimonials. On such matters as birth control many Catholics are unable to engage in justifiable debate but, rather, can only parrot or paraphrase stereotyped dogma. This all too common illustration exemplifies the manner in which a well-ingrained religious background can preclude logical thinking. It also demonstrates the religious fail-safe in action: it stands to reason that if a person, when challenged by alien ideas, is able automatically to react to the threat, he can reject the foreign argument without even having to ponder it. The fail-safe operates as a guarantee that the dogmatic thinking process will be ongoing and self-perpetuating; it is a religiously founded, intricate system of unwritten rules by which a person is to accept or reject new ideas.

I will note here that the fail-safe is such a very real and adhesive entity that during psychiatric treatment it is seldom tampered with but is avoided and circumvented. Other fail-safes that do not have a religious foundation seem to be more approachable in therapy. It is the sacred aura around the religious fail-safe that makes any tampering taboo. Patients tend to overreact to any introspection or to questioning of their religious beliefs.

In short, the fail-safe is a "rejector" of new information and ideas, while the filter effect is a "distorter" of new information and ideas.

As these rejecting and distorting religious mechanisms operate, the maturing child assumes a position of relative isolation from the outside world. He has, through his religious upbringing, accumulated a system of intrinsic attitudes that are quite unlike extrinsic reality. (His less religious counterpart is not likely to be troubled by such a dichotomy.) Furthermore, because his distorted perceptions force him to live and react within the extrinsic real world, a polarization of his personality footing results.

(The child who is strongly indoctrinated with religious influences has a personality that can be compared to a magnet with two opposing and repelling poles: reality at one end, religious dogma at the other.)

The stage is thus set for an infinite mass of double messages, and these can be too much for the mind to reconcile comfortably. One side of each double message or concept is the intrinsic prejudice of religion; the other side is the extrinsic actuality of life itself. The following common examples demonstrate the preceding:

Example 1: intrinsic: Jewish attitudes; extrinsic: Gentile environment

It is early December and the Jewish child is again reminded that he does not believe in Christ; nevertheless, he is immersed in a milieu of Christmas celebration. He is surrounded by Christmas at school and almost everywhere else he ventures, even his own home in many instances (many "modern" Jewish families incorporate Christmas trees as seasonal home decorations). At school he may even have the opportunity of singing in the Christmas chorus or playing the part of a Wise Man.

In spite of all this environmental immersion, he is taught at home that Christmas is really a kind of humbug; that Christ really was not what he was cracked up to have been; and that Hanukkah is a better holiday anyway, since on Hanukkah it is the tradition to receive more presents (in many Jewish families it is traditional that the children receive a gift on each of the eight days of Hanukkah).

Though this common double bind may seem inconsequential and even amusing, I can assure you that it is not. The consequences are numerous and significant for the child who is placed into the seemingly innocuous situation I have just described. To him, Christmas becomes a very desirable but untouchable humbug, and his parents become the "Scrooges" who deter him from this forbidden fruit.

A polarization is taking place not only between the child and his parents but between the child and his peers as well. Around Christmastime Jewish children often seduce Gentile peers into a harsh controversy about the existence or nonexistence of Santa Claus and Holy Spirits. The debate stems from the Jewish child's own envy of his Gentile friends' culture. It is a pitiful sour-grapes attitude: in actuality, he wishes he too could have Christmas but rationalizes that the holiday is ill-founded and that he is therefore better off without it.

However, the worst plight of this Jewish child is caused not by parent or peer but by something more intensely uncomfortable. He is plagued by a feeling of being dispossessed from his environment, as though he were looking in from the outside. He feels left out and forgotten during a time of year when people most want to be remembered. If he is living in a small town with a disproportionately small Jewish population, this phenomenon is considerably exaggerated.

I use Christmas as an example here because it is during this holiday that the "outsider feeling" becomes most prominent. However, I do not mean to overlook that this tug of emotions occurs during the entire year, only to be further exacerbated during the holidays of the Gentile world. So intense can this affection (or feeling) be that it can stimulate the child to fantasize that he is not Jewish. The child carries this feeling with him into adulthood, where its adverse effects may become more apparent.

In adulthood the fantasy of being "non-Jewish" is combined with a wish to become assimilated by the Gentile world. Often the Jew discovers that total acclimatization to the Gentile community is impossible; he finds it difficult to establish more than superficial friendships in a world from which he continues to feel separated. Some find the dilemma so painful that they proceed to denounce their religion or convert from it.

Regardless of what they do to solve the conflict of feeling like outsiders, they rarely really adjust happily. The attempted compromise between Jewish identity and the non-Jewish environment often leads to mixed feelings at best.

A paradoxical reaction may beset the entire Jewish family at Christmastime. It is common for Jewish children to rebel against parents with a kind of religious backlash. I recall a family who erected a Christmas tree by the decree of the father, mother, and two of the younger children. The oldest child felt that this was distasteful and sacrilegious. The resulting polarization was so extreme that all friendly communication between the oldest child and the remainder of the family ceased.

As I have illustrated by this first set of examples, a conflict need not be confined within a person; it may develop into a cleavage between family members or even between sections of an entire community.

The next example will provide another look at a head-on collision between intrinsic and extrinsic religious attitudes within the confines of a single family.

Example 2: intrinsic: literal interpretation of Mormon dicta; extrinsic: liberal interpretation of Mormon dicta

I would like to discuss a family in which a man of the Mormon persuasion marries a Catholic woman who, for the sake of family unity, converts to Mormonism. Prior to the time when their seven-year-old daughter was enrolled in Sunday School, the Mormon dictum of alcoholic abstinence was overlooked. The couple often enjoyed a round of drinks before dinner and then wine during dinner. After a year of religious training the daughter began to object to this on the grounds that it was sinful. The embarrassed couple responded immediately with curtailment of their drinking; so from the child's vantage point, intrinsic wishes were fulfilled through the extrinsic change in parental habits. In this case the parents are bowing to the child's demand that they change an aspect of their lifestyle.

The psychological implications of this situation can be ominous. Referring to the work of psychoanalysts, it is generally accepted that children have an active fantasy life and that in their fantasies many impossible wishes can come true. The fantasy or daydream vicariously fulfills wishes that cannot be granted in real life. The daydream may seem so real to the child that just the thought of something is equivalent to the actual experiencing of it. For example, a child imagining that he is or wishing to be an astronaut may momentarily feel as though he has become an astronaut. The daydream in a young child, then, is like a magic wishing machine that responds to every whim.

As the child grows, however, he is gradually able to learn that his daydreams are not the magic they once were. He can no longer be what he wants to be or get what he wants to get merely by thinking. This gradual introduction to reality is an important part of growing up that must occur in anyone who is to become mentally healthy in adulthood.

How does all this apply to our example of the young girl dictating rules of living to her parents?

The girl has a wish that Daddy and Mommy will conform to her ways of thinking as dictated by her Sunday School teachers. She expresses to her parents the wish that they discontinue their "sinful" drinking and, like magic, her wish is fulfilled. The disturbing concept is that the daughter has assumed actual power to manipulate her parents.

This reversal of family authority is a result of the injection of religious authority into the family via the daughter. In the eyes of the daughter the manipulated parents have lost some of their influence as family leaders; not only has the daughter assumed inappropriate "powers" over her parents, but the church has assumed power over the entire family.

Significantly, the daughter's renewed magical powers may eventually give rise to feelings of guilt because she has been able to force her parents to alter the course of their living habits. She thus loses track of the realistic boundaries of her powers. She will be encouraged to expect that other wishes and whims will similarly be granted.

Later, if in the course of an argument with her mother she wishes for her mother to die, will her mother respond to this wish also? Will the daughter be able to use her parentally sanctioned authority wisely in the future? Is she deserving of such family control? These are a few inevitable questions that might plague this girl if the imbalance of family authority (backed by religious authority) is allowed to continue.

Herein lies the potential source of guilt feelings for this girl. This is why a child should not be granted authority to control his parents' behavior. While it is certainly favorable to allow a child reasonable household responsibilities, it is detrimental to allow him to usurp any of those responsibilities that rightfully belong to the parents. There is a danger of this happening whenever parents who are themselves apathetic to religion enroll a child in intensive religious schooling. It should be obvious that these conditions are not uncommon.

The other side of the coin in the same case history might also have undesirable implications. Had the practice of social drinking in this household continued, there would have been a fostering of ambivalent messages to the child from parents and church. A kind of split in authority would have occurred, forcing the daughter to choose sides between parents and church. These conditions also exist commonly and lead to profound confusion for the child. It can easily lead to a fostering of ambivalent attitudes toward the parents' drinking habits and toward the parents themselves.

The result may be a dilution of parental respect against a backdrop of church mores; the child will then find it difficult to identify with or emulate his parents (something that should occur within a healthy family constellation). This ultimately leads to difficulty for the child in discovering his own sense of identity at adolescence.

The preceding examples have a tragic similarity. Religion in these cases either served as a destructive influence or was experienced as an uncomfortable feeling. As I shall detail later, this need not be the case; religion potentially can be a very enriching and supportive life experience. It is the *misuse* of religion that is a deterrent to development and a hazard to health. Though I could cite endless further examples, I would summarize that religion, even when loosely practiced by a family, can ultimately, in the context of the environment, give rise to an inordinate number of double messages to growing children. These messages confuse and frustrate children and often lead to feelings of guilt. This can do nothing less than inhibit, to a varying degree, the normal healthy process of emotional growth.

The mentally healthy adolescent, on the threshold of his

independent life, must possess many qualifications to meet unknown future challenges. He must be flexible in his thinking as he approaches and masters new kinds of work and meets and deals with all kinds of people. He must therefore have adaptability so that he might take on a great many challenges without the impediment of baseline prejudices dating back to childhood. He will be better suited to think and act flexibly and innovatively if he is able to mature in a flexible mold—a mold that itself can change as needed. His thinking abilities logically extend further if they are not closed in by boundary lines and ill-founded taboos—which introduces my next point.

One might ask why, with so many religions available, is there not one that, for a given person, will contribute to (rather than detract from) emotional growth? The question can be answered from many viewpoints; I choose to approach it from a psychogenetic point of view.

The conception of almost every new human being involves the coming together of forty-six genetic units (chromosomes) that contain the information required to produce and direct the formation of that human being. That is: the father and mother, via their sperm and egg respectively, each contribute twenty-three of these genetic units from his or her stockpile, which contains parts of forty-six chromosomes. The possible combinations of the genetic factors selected numbers in the billions. Suffice it to say that the selection of these forty-six chromosomes, which are to provide for the offspring's genetic makeup, is like the selection of forty-six grains of sand from two large sandboxes. The resulting child, then, in every case (with the exception only of identical twins) is a unique miracle. He may resemble his brother or someone else in the family, but these resemblances, biologically speaking, are mere superficialities.

Added to this infinity of biological variation is environmental variation, which is of equal importance in contributing to human individualities. The growing child will be molded and guided by these genetic-environmental influences. The biological determinants were established long before birth, so very little can be done to change them. The profound environmental influences, however, are provided and controlled throughout childhood by the parents, who, via their actions, reactions, and examples, help to form the human mold.

Religion, through the parents, is often allowed to become part of this mold and therefore provides profound influences on growth. It becomes apparent that no religion can be so unusual that it becomes a totally complementary part of this peerless mold. In fact, it would be naïve to surmise that the selection of one religion out of a hundred will have a positive effect on any particular child who has been biologically selected from a pool of billions of chromosome combinations.

What does all this eventually mean to the developing child? Relatively little has been written about what is a mentally healthy adult, perhaps because mental health is less interesting to study than mental illness. I cannot claim to have an all-inclusive definition of what "mentally healthy" is, but I think it generally holds true that a person with a healthy mind possesses certain characteristics. Some of these are inherent, others materialize only in the context of the environment, and are thus sociological.

In the mainstream of our society a healthy person is one who, much of the time, is able to enjoy living and can continue doing so, and not at the expense of others. He is able to derive independent happiness (within himself) as well as interdependent happiness (with a spouse, friends, etc.). Moreover, he is able to tolerate reasonably stressful situations, should they arise; he is able to set and achieve reasonable goals and to interact successfully with people while en route to his goals.

Of special concern to me is that a healthy individual, within the limits of his physical and mental capacities, be able to adapt to the new life situations as these develop. He must be able, through this adaptation, to meet and deal with the inevitable obstacles.

Ideally, the child has been allowed to blossom within a mold that allows room for every petal to form. Thoughtful parents can constantly alter this pliable mold to allow for the unique variations of their offspring. Only in this way can they more closely meet his needs and respond to him warmly and sensitively. In this process the parents themselves will grow; they are essentially like sculptors, meticulously working with the ultimate of building materials— their own protoplasm.

Religion has a most definite part to play in this complex matrix.

Three questions are appropriate here:

1. Can religion be responsive enough to meet the sensitivity of a unique child?
2. Can an archaic and complex system of ideas and attitudes enhance the delicate growth process?
3. Can such an influence be healthy for the maturing child who is characteristically so pliable?

In many instances religion at its best is not harmful but does discourage creative and adaptive thinking. That this has literally happened in an historic sense is exemplified by the Catholic Church's unwillingness to accept, in the days of the great Galileo, that the world is round. Galileo was condemned for heresy by the Church. The resistances of contemporary religion are not so obvious but are present nonetheless. Religion's clouding of present-day thinking and imagination is exercising a destructive influence on the masses in every part of the world.

Suffice it to say that it seldom provides a major positive influence on the normal process of emotional development that, it is hoped, leads to mental health. In most cases it has not done so and cannot, for it is too rigid and can almost never change rapidly enough. Though religion may at one time have served man, man now is serving religion, and often at his own expense. He puts up with its teachings until they become intolerable and/or preposterous. He then modifies it to make it a little less intolerable, and therefore it never really catches up and never really serves, but demands service. Religion demands service by dictating rules to be followed and sacrifices to be made, but often gives very little to its followers in return.

There is a possible Yes or No answer for each of the preceding three questions. Though I gravitate toward the negative, affirmative answers are possible; these can occur, however, only when a thoughtful parent carefully introduces religion to his children in a reasonable and palatable form (see Chapter 7).

3

Religion and Emotional Instability

Axiom 1 serves as a premise for this axiom, which was partially alluded to in the previous chapter:

Axiom 2: Rigid, confined, and stereotyped religious thinking patterns can be directly contributory to emotional instability. Here it takes the form of a health hazard in a psychiatric sense.

With the help of a hospital case history, this chapter will show how religion can have a profound influence leading to significant emotional problems.

The person who lacks the ability to adjust to life frustrations will have much difficulty in maintaining his emotional stability. The subjective alternate feelings of pleasure and frustration (or pain) are a part of normal maturation; we learn to adapt by learning to seek the former and avoid or tolerate the latter. As some frustration and anxiety are generally thought to be necessary for learning, attempts to reduce these unpleasantries artificially might lead to a reduced future ability to adjust or adapt.

Throughout a person's life one very real source of frustration can be the great number of unanswered philosophical questions about the meaning of life. I prefer to think of these questions as man's ultimate inquiries or frustrations. They are ultimate not only in a religious-philosophical sense, but in a psychiatric sense also; for if one has no reasonable answers to these questions, one may indeed be depressed or even suicidal.

The questions I refer to are:

Who am I?

How did I get here?

How should I live?

Where am I going?

Why am I going there?

Where am I going after I have been there?

If a person can independently find satisfactory answers, he will possess the essential ingredients to promote stability in his life. If, however, he seeks out preset arbitrary answers from the church, there will be two effects:

1.   His frustration and anxiety will have been reduced or extinguished.
2.   He will not have found it necessary to think through these questions to his own satisfaction and therefore shall have learned nothing about himself.

As religion is so often preoccupied with rigid arbitrary answers to these ponderings, the religious person need not figure these things out for himself. And since religion's preset answers were in most cases given centuries ago and were intended to apply to many people, they in effect miss the mark in adequately answering anything for anyone today. Eventually this can adversely affect a person's mental health, as shown in the following case history.

Case History 1

Angela, fifty-one years old, was admitted to the mental health unit of a general hospital with sundry complaints, but she was primarily preoccupied by a "bulge" on her right arm. The patient was noted to be intensely anxious and severely depressed, but on physical examination no "bulge" of any kind was found. It was generally agreed by the staff psychiatrists that the patient's *imagined* physical defect was really representative of some displaced anxieties over current problems. (Such a preoccupation with physical complaints is a common mechanism used to alleviate emotional problems. The person may or may not actually be aware that he is using such a mechanism.)

After a series of psychiatric interviews it became apparent that the patient's anxiety and depression began when her son was about to embark on his college career in a small town seven hundred miles away. This was to be Angela's first prolonged separation from her son. Angela was unable to face this problem without intense feelings of uneasiness; she therefore chose to focus on an imaginary symptom in order to displace her thinking away from the son. So deep-seated was her depression that she was incapacitated, even with regard to doing simple household tasks.

Of prime significance in this patient's past history was the fact that she had always lived a very meticulous and perfectionist kind of life. This was reflected in almost every aspect of her lifestyle: she had always been a compulsive housekeeper and had also labored excessively at her bookkeeping job with a local accounting firm. Her supervisor had often commented that the patient refused to take coffee breaks and would waste time cleaning her desk and the office, even though a full-time janitor was employed to do this.

The patient recalled that she had lived a life closely bound to the Methodist religion, which she had learned to interpret in a very literal way since childhood. She had been a regular churchgoer as long as she could recollect and usually spent five to ten hours a week reading the New Testament. Though her adherence to the church had always been strong, she had recently become much more involved with it.

Simultaneous with this increased indulgence in church work and Bible-reading the patient's marriage deteriorated. Her husband was a free-lance construction worker, and through a mutually agreed upon arrangement with his wife, he began working more and more on out-of-town construction projects. In addition, the couple's sexual relationship had recently all but ceased.

In the course of several therapy sessions Angela expressed repeatedly to me her strong regard for morals and her incessant need to carry on a righteous life "in the eyes of God." She went on to say that God had always been good to her and to her family and that she had repaid Him by inculcating her son with religion. Though apparently cooperative and candid most of the time, the patient neglected to mention to me that she had been admitted to the state mental hospital four years earlier. This very significant but unmentioned history was related to me by the patient's husband and was later documented by the state hospital's records.

Just before that hospitalization she had behaved very atypically for a period lasting approximately one month. During that time, she went through episodes of wandering from one local bar to another, drinking excessively, and seducing any man who would tolerate her. This behavior was particularly inappropriate for this woman, who had led a life of total abstinence from alcohol, promiscuity, and other church-forbidden activities. It was interesting that even subtle questioning of the patient about this dramatic incident in her history proved fruitless.

This case history is of great significance because in some degree it is commonly repeated in families who live closely bound to a fundamentalist Protestantism. In studying the anatomy of this patient's plight, many things become apparent. She had lived a very difficult life, with much sacrificing every step of the way. Since early childhood, she was forced to contribute to the family income and the church represented her only outside activity. Guided by tenacious religious teachings, she always "knew" that a good, clean, proper life would someday pay off: avoidance of sin was reassurance of eventual salvation. She assumed that dedication to the church would cancel out her realization that her marriage was suffering and that her life had a poverty of direction.

While proceeding through life, she had been able to resist and overcome frequent temptation to do "wrong." She avoided church taboos to the letter and was confident of an ultimate reward. She always felt a duty to her marriage (not her husband) because it was sanctified in the church and therefore was of itself sacred. She took pride in having recently "celebrated" her twenty-fifth wedding anniversary.

In her self-righteous existence she entered a cycle: she lived by the church and was reciprocally rewarded by it—with tokenism. The reward was abstract but existent nevertheless: as she carefully listened to each Sunday sermon, she was able to hold her head high, reassuring herself and others that she lived up to the very ideals and rules being preached. This in itself serves as a major kind of reward for this kind of person.

Another part of the cycle was the patient's role in the family as a teacher or perpetuator of Methodist ideals, which in turn made her look even better "in the eyes of God." This cycle of self-righteousness is self-propelled because it intrinsically rewards a person; the cycle is one of artificial martyrdom.

Unhappily, the cycle can be self-limiting, and when it stops, the results are devastating, as in Angela's case. Being jarred out of a lifelong religious habit pattern can be compared to ending a drug habit "cold turkey." The withdrawal symptoms may be just as uncomfortable for the victim. For any one of a thousand reasons the whole cycle can break down.

In the lives of most people tragedy is an infrequent but inevitable occurrence. (Angela's dramatic drinking and sexual binge suddenly followed the unexpected death of her oldest brother.) Few people get through life without losing a mother, father, or other loved person. Perhaps the tragedy takes the form of a lost job, a physical disability, or a divorce. These events, potentially depressing experiences in anyone's life, are even more tragic for a person of Angela's type.

She was much less equipped to cope with tragedy because it did not fit well into her detailed scheme of life, a scheme that now has proven to be anything but realistic. Her meticulous piety has not paid off as expected; her avoidance of sin did nothing to immunize her against the dread consequences of her son's leaving and brother's dying. She suddenly has discovered that others who have scorned her compulsive ways may indeed lead relatively rich lives.

She also has found that no one is going to praise her forever for the good life she has led; and during the first hospitalization she discovered that her vulnerability to tragedy is no less than that of her neighbors, who frequently "sin." The very beliefs she has clutched at so strongly have let her down. She had been led to believe that her "good" life and church involvement would result in happiness. Not only did this fail, but during the hospitalization, Angela's preoccupation with religious material impeded her psychotherapy.

Rather than discuss her own problems, she preferred to talk about the avoidance of sin and forgiveness of God. The pragmatist who assumes that tragedy will strike, deservedly or not, is therefore somewhat ready to deal with it. But the strong fundamental teachings of Angela's religion only protected her stability with a thin paper wall; it had always appeared structurally competent—until it was put to the test.

Angela was less adaptable than she should have been when adaptability was necessary. Her wall began to rip like confetti at the thought of her son leaving for college. She entered the hospital with severe depression over the occurrence that would merely have brought a few tears to the eyes of most mothers. This patient will *always* have relative difficulty in meeting even minor crises.

A second characteristic demonstrated by this unfortunate woman is the all-or-none phenomenon. The latter (none) was demonstrated by her strict lifelong adherence to set rules in spite of her inherent drives to want to do otherwise. She was able to maintain her moralistic front successfully for an exceedingly long time; for forty-seven years she did not break rules and maintained the "none" phenomenon. This can, as in this instance, be tolerable for long periods of time—indeed, for some people it can last a lifetime.

But in many instances when a person can no longer tolerate a "none" life, the alternative is the "all" life. Angela lived a life of chastity and abstinence from all forms of "sin" for forty-seven years—until her life situation became intolerable. She then, in the wake of tragedy, suddenly transgressed into an emotional reaction, manifested by promiscuity and excessive drinking. Her transition into the "all" phenomenon represented the acting-out of many needs that had always been present but were completely suppressed under a blanket of religious taboos.

Like many other people, she was unable to continue the suppression of normal impulses as prescribed by her inflexible religious upbringing. Her topheavy conscience toppled quickly when natural impulses became too strong. Angela represents a commonly seen tragedy that is the result of religious overindulgence early in life. Unlike Angela, many overindulgers are able to contain their inherent drives permanently. Though they may not become emotionally ill, as she did, many of them remain in a lifelong state of relative misery.

Angela's case history can be restated in the condensed form of the following axiom.

Axiom 3:   Profound lifelong religious indoctrination may assume the form of a punitive conscience in the adult. This serves to stifle the person's conscious recognition of normal drives; he is therefore unable to deal with them in times of stress.

The chances are that Angela will continue to have problems long after she has returned home from the hospital.

She has a distinct disadvantage over many other patients in therapy: the "filter effect" and "fail-safe" are operating against her. These will act as built-in barriers to suggestions or inquiries made by her psychiatrist. He will have to work around these barriers, like a quarterback avoiding the defensive linemen. If he were ever mistakenly to challenge this patient's religious adherence, a stalemate in psychotherapy would probably result.

It would be unfair to end this example without an outline of an alternative life course that Angela could have taken to avoid her emotional malady. Had she led a somewhat more permissive life, she might have realized that, like other people, she had basic drives and a need to deal with them. Then she could have vented these impulses in more gradual and socially acceptable ways. A byproduct would have been the incidental life pleasures derived from gratification of her drives. This would have been a more realistic and healthy approach, and a less burdening one.

Had she been presented this alternative early in life, her episode of bizarre behavior at age forty-seven and depression at age fifty-one might have been prevented. More important, if she had been allowed to grow up under a more reasonable influence than her punitive religion, she might have enjoyed a richer life with her husband. Because of her preoccupation with sin and church activity, she virtually ignored him sexually through most of their marriage. It developed that her attitudes about sex were remnants of fire-and-brimstone sermons, as well as of her mother's slanted Biblical reinterpretations. People with a background such as Angela's are often known for their long, faithful, but empty marriages.

I would add a footnote: Angela's problems were anything but an accident. They are the collective result of a group of causal factors; they are a very predictable result of religion at its worst. Her case exemplifies the use of religion as a kind of stick with which a person administers a self-beating for no apparent reason. The result of this chronic beating is emotional instability in a relatively mild form.

Having demonstrated some effects of religion on the thinking process and the development of emotional instability, I will discuss the role of religion in psychotic behavior.

4

Religion and the Psychoses

There is a common, close association between religion and psychotic disorders. I once knew a psychologist who said that it was beyond his imagination how a person could be raised as a Pentecostal and avoid becoming a paranoid schizophrenic. Though he was certainly exaggerating, there is a significant grain of truth in his statement.

Before demonstrating religion's role in psychotic illnesses, some general discussion about psychoses is in order. Pragmatically speaking, psychosis refers to a group of psychiatric disorders that share certain common characteristics. The disorder is always a profound one because it will completely disrupt the sufferer's life at times; it may even incapacitate him totally.

A psychotic person, at least some of the time, is relatively out of touch with reality. He may live in his own world of fantasy and terror much of the time. His perceptions may be so altered that he tends to overinterpret or misinterpret everything in his environment. There may be extreme vacillations in his mood, so that at one time he appears overtly, but artificially, happy and at another time greatly depressed. His detachment from reality may include a detachment from his own self: he actually loses his identity and is consequently unaware of who he is.

Psychosis has any number of causes and can occur essentially at almost any age, taking on different characteristics that are sometimes especially common at a particular age. Some psychotic disturbances may have a purely organic or physiological cause, perhaps from the use of drugs (for example, LSD-induced psychotic reactions); withdrawal from drugs (for example, delirium tremens occurring during withdrawal from chronic alcohol intake); physical illnesses (for example, senility resulting from advanced atherosclerosis); from injuries to the brain (for example, a concussion sustained in an automobile accident). In all of these examples the cause, or etiology, is very clear-cut; this is not the case in other kinds of psychoses, such as the schizophrenic variety.

Schizophrenia is a psychotic disorder that unfortunately is very common and exhibits many of those characteristics previously described. For decades psychiatrists have been speculating about what causes this illness, and opinion is divided. Some experts feel that this disease entity is caused by an imbalance in the body's biochemistry; others feel that it may be an inherited defect; still others feel that submicroscopic anatomical lesions may be at fault.

At the other extreme of speculation are psychiatrists who feel that schizophrenia is a result only of the pathological environment within which the victim has matured. Increasingly, contemporary feeling is that a combination of any of these factors can lead to this illness. Many doctors, in fact, believe that no person is completely invulnerable to schizophrenia. I agree that the latter statements hold true for schizophrenia (and for other psychotic disorders as well).

Moreover, I will show how religion can act as an environmental factor contributing to psychosis.

Religion shows its effects on psychosis in many ways: it can precipitate a psychosis, become the central theme of such a reaction, or lay the groundwork in rendering a person susceptible to such a reaction. The next case history demonstrates religion precipitating a psychotic illness.

Case History 2

Luke, a twenty-nine-year-old, was brought into the hospital by his wife, who complained that he had not been functioning well. He was employed as a janitor in a textile mill; on the day prior to his hospital admission he arrived at work, sat in front of his locker, and appeared to be staring out into space.

A fellow worker inquired if he could be of some help. The patient replied, "Well, I think to a certain extent, but maybe not anyway."

He continued to talk in nonsense phrases and was taken to the company nurse's office. After a short interview there, psychiatric consultation was recommended. When I first interviewed Luke in the hospital, he was sitting rigidly in a chair, staring at the wall. He seemed to be quite confused, totally disoriented, and completely preoccupied with his own thoughts. His responses even to simple questions were totally inappropriate and I therefore consulted his wife for some background history.

According to her, Luke had always been somewhat shy as a child and had some difficulty establishing close relationships with people. He had always seemed to enjoy being alone and would spend much of his time daydreaming. Little else is really known of his childhood. Later in life he was a hard-working man and a good provider, especially during most of his three-year marriage.

The patient's unusual behavior became noticeable to his wife a little more than two years previously, when the couple became involved in the Pentecostal religion. Just prior to his involvement with that church group, he was somewhat disenchanted with the direction in which his life was moving and was reaching out for help.

At that time a friend at his work suggested active church participation as a possible means of finding happiness. Shortly after his introduction to and participation in this fundamentalist church, Luke's behavior showed signs of change. He began praying aloud with highly charged emotions, crying, and displaying considerable bodily animation. Prior to this time Luke could be described as having been essentially unemotional. His new preoccupation with religion included a great deal of Bible-reading and what the patient's wife described as "visions" (I choose to refer to the latter as hallucinations).

Along with this radical behavioral change came a heightened interest in sexual activity. Previously the couple engaged in sexual intercourse once weekly. More recently Luke had insisted on daily sexual relations, with the exception of Sunday "because sex was sinful." For some time prior to his hospitalization Luke had been hearing voices, seeing his "visions," and once had made a phone call to someone he thought was Joseph, Jesus' father.

He had become very suspicious of his wife's handling of their financial affairs and felt that a realtor had cheated the couple on their recent purchase of a home. A week prior to his hospital admission Luke threatened a fellow worker with a knife; his motive for this was founded on groundless suspicion.

After one week in the hospital on medications this patient was again able to speak in a coherent fashion, though his judgment remained impaired. He told me at that time of his unhappiness and of his desire to leave the hospital and to go home to his wife and his "Holy Roller Church." Luke was convinced that his problems could be approached only through the church, via forgiveness by the Holy Spirit.

At the request of this patient, his wife, and his father, he was discharged from the hospital, but against my medical advice. Three days later he attempted a return to work, but was unable to tolerate this for more than twenty minutes or so. One week after his hospital discharge I received a call from his mother, who sounded desperate for help. Luke had again become hyperemotional and threatening, and was obviously in immediate need of rehospitalization. It was evident to me that long-term hospitalization was probably now indicated, and so I recommended to her that she avail herself of the state hospital facilities for Luke.

It is tragically obvious that Luke's illness is of much greater severity than Angela's. Unlike Angela, he became totally detached from reality at times, experienced hallucinations, and had delusions of persecution. On at least one occasion he even became potentially dangerous because of his lack of judgment.

Luke experienced an almost complete disintegration of his personality. As with Angela, however, the evolving mental illness was at some point guided or effected by indulgence in religious thinking and activity. To overlook this fact would be to ignore basic reality in these cases.

I would be presumptuous to suggest that Luke's illness was simply caused by his introduction to the Pentecostal church activities; this certainly was not the case. A combination of many influences was responsible for his deterioration. I think it is generally fair to say that because of genetic factors and/or aspects of his childhood rearing, Luke developed a propensity to become psychotic or, more specifically, schizophrenic. The fact that as a child he preferred solitude and daydreaming to social interaction lends support to this conclusion and suggests that his grip on reality may always have been tenuous. Religion did not cause this man's illness; rather, religion served as a heavy straw that fractured the camel's personality. This can be more appropriately summarized in the form of another axiom.

Axiom 4: If a person has a tenuous grasp on reality, highly charged religious happenings may create an illusion of unreality within him. This, in turn, may serve to sever his weak connection with reality, thus precipitating a psychotic reaction.

Before concluding that Luke's history supports this axiom, three factors must be examined:

1. Luke's previous general personality makeup.
2. His emotional stability just prior to becoming involved with the church.
3. The character and consequences of Pentecostalism, people in general and Luke specifically.

As to the first factor, Luke had obvious personality problems throughout most of his known early life. He was a shy boy, somewhat withdrawn at times, and considered to have been of slightly lower than average intelligence. According to his mother, however, he had never apparently lost contact with reality. He was able to function in high school, though his grades were only Cs and Ds. He had been emotionally competent enough to meet a girl, marry her, and father a child. During his marriage, he held a steady job and earned enough money to subsist and to assume a home mortgage. In summary, he had been a person who, though limited in social and vocational abilities, was able to live and work within the confines of reality.

As to Luke's stability just prior to church involvement, life was becoming more difficult to face. Subjectively, he felt somewhat depressed and was searching for some meaning in life at that critical time. His new responsibilities of becoming a father and homeowner became added sources of stress, which was difficult to tolerate. It was at this critical point that Luke turned to a close friend for advice; he then chose to become active in a fundamentalist church movement in an attempt to achieve happiness and some meaning for his existence.

Before a description of the mechanics of a Pentecostal kind of religious service, some information about this spiritual movement is useful. The original historical-religious significance dates back to ancient Judaism, when the Pentecost referred to the fiftieth day following the second day of Passover. The day served as a kind of sacrificial harvest celebration during which offerings were made. Much later the Christian church modified the celebration to refer to the descent of the Holy Spirit upon the apostles.

More recently (and of more immediate importance), Pentecostalism has become associated with a kind of religious, hyperexcited state of mind, characterized by ecstatic outcrying and concomitant emotional excitement. The movement has also been associated with the "gift of tongues" concept, which, simply stated, is a power granted by the Holy Spirit to enable one to be understood by a congregation whose individual members are unable to converse in the same language. Via this "gift of tongues" the preacher may be wailing unintelligible sounds, which are interpreted by each member of the congregation in his own language.

This entire concept is a type of collective delusion shared by the gathering. The desired result of all this is, in a manner of speaking, a spiritual orgasm. During such religious gatherings the air is almost permeated with a kind of electrical emotionalism that is infectious. At the peak of such an orgastic experience an almost convulsive regression of the person's thought processes occurs: he transiently departs from reality. He begins feeling, to the exclusion of thinking; orientation and judgment are quickly diminished.

I am able to describe the content of such a fundamentalist service both from my own subjective experience at such a service and from a compendium of descriptions by several of my current patients. The general theme of such a religious happening is emotion, conveyed in two forms: fear and elation. The preacher in one of his performances exudes large amounts of fear in the form of emotionally charged Biblically founded threats about going to hell, etc. He utilizes the Bible as an authority to frighten his congregation away from sin. One need only glance at the faces of the congregation to assess the efficacy of such preachment: indeed, many appear frantic. I have on occasion noted a great increase in my own pulse, respiration, and sweating while attending such a happening.

Just as fear is emitted from such a pulpit, so is elation. The deft preacher with impressive charisma can uplift the entire gathering by wailing profound optimisms about the recoming of God, reawakening of the people, and salvation. I have seen large portions of congregations moved from actual tears of despair to happiness and euphoria at the mere whim of the preacher. Such a religious service, then, is one of high temperament, with wide mood swings regulated by a very powerful leader.

Such profound emotional variation creates an intense feeling of unreality within the active participator. If he is at all naïve, the experience can be temporarily frightening or uplifting. If, on the other hand, the person is seriously prone to emotional instability, the consequences may be grave. A series of such religious services, or even a single one of them, can—and often does—precipitate a psychotic reaction in such an individual.

Luke was just such a person. Throughout his childhood he was known to have been somewhat emotionally abnormal, but it was not until he became intensely involved with church activities that he became psychotic. After several months of attending highly charged church services he slipped rapidly from the real world.

At first his abnormal behavior was limited to the physical confines of the church services, but as time progressed he gradually brought the effect of the church services home and to the hospital. He was helpless to turn off what the preacher had turned on. Religious experiences became a full-time obsession, enhancing his transition from reality to unreality, from neurosis to psychosis. Given the slightest stress at home, he reacted with emotional praying, accompanied by wild bodily gyrations. This became "his" world of reality, set quite apart from others.

I would like to answer some inevitable criticism about the validity of my conclusions from this case history. Speculation might have it that I have misconstrued the cause and effect of Luke's illness. Do people get sick partially as a result of their religious participation or do sick people gravitate toward certain religions?

Certainly, many followers of ultrafundamentalist religious practices have ongoing emotional difficulties. These religious groups have a magnetic attraction for such people and in fact often fulfill some needs for them. I have met many such people at their gatherings and have concluded that a significant minority of them and their clergy are psychotic, while much of the remaining majority are burdened with significant psychiatric problems.

There is absolutely no question in my mind that many ultrafundamentalist preachers are themselves suffering from a schizophrenic psychosis.

Suffice it for now to say that many practicing religious ultrafundamentalists were victims of emotional illness prior to active church interaction. For these people the cause of illness must be found elsewhere. (It is important, though, to interpose that many of these people sought such religious practices as an attempt to alleviate their significant problems. I wonder how their lives might have been changed had they sought psychiatric help instead of taking a religious plunge.)

While I readily admit that many ultrafundamentalists are initially disturbed and became fundamentalists via a natural-selection process, many others become emotionally disturbed only after their intense religious exposure. Luke is a case in point. At a time when he was experiencing difficulties with life, he chose immersion into a radical religion as a way out. Rather than finding solace, he was induced, with the aid of misused religion, to escape almost totally from the world of actuality. The content of his delusions and hallucinations (violent praying aloud and "visions") documents this development.

The preceding clearly demonstrates how religion may precipitate a psychotic reaction in a person who has a latent propensity for it. Another effect of religion on psychotic behavior was also suggested and will be enlarged upon with the next axiom and the case history that follows.

Axiom 5: A pathological effect of religion on a psychotic person is commonly manifested in his delusional system; that is, Biblical material often provides the theme and variations that are the content of a psychotic episode.

Case History 3

Paul is a twenty-eight-year-old who was brought to the hospital emergency room by his wife, who complained that his recent behavior was bizarre. The patient had been well only two months before. Paul was a fundamentalist Baptist who was raised in an intensely concentrated religious milieu. Quite recently he had joined a new Baptist church and had experienced a veritable renaissance of interest in Bible-reading and his rediscovered faith.

His wife reported that he was spending from four to six hours a night indulging in Bible-reading at the expense of his usual habits of watching television, visiting with her, and playing with his four children. Approximately three months before this, the patient had attempted to enlist in the Air Force Officer Candidate School, but was turned down because of poor eyesight. It was indeed a paradox that Paul, when called by his draft board two months later, applied for conscientious-objector status and was, not surprisingly, turned down; he was then ordered to report for active duty within thirty days. It seems that this stressful event directly precipitated Paul's current symptoms.

Early on the day of hospitalization he left as always for his classes at a local junior college, but returned home at two o'clock, three hours earlier than usual. As he entered the house he began to shout Biblical phrases at his wife and children and expressed the determined intention to baptize each of them. Upon realizing that his wife was reluctant to participate in this ritual, he began to beg and gently plead with her, and he expressed the feeling that baptism was so very necessary for the cleansing of her "sins."

It was at this point that she initiated the arrangements for Paul's hospitalization. Because he arrived at the hospital late at night, it was not until the following morning that I saw him. As I walked off the elevator I immediately noticed this young man kneeling in the doorway of his room, absorbed in prayer. As I approached him he quickly rose and very humbly asked if I would let him baptize me. When I gently refused this, he knelt at my feet and proceeded in a dramatic fashion to plead with me to accept his baptismal rites. He told me that it would take but a moment and that I would be cleansed of all sin.

I then attempted to interview the man but the effort was, for the most part, discouraging and unproductive. He spoke exclusively in Biblical phraseology with liberal use of words such as "wouldst," "thou," "ye," and so on, and used such sentences as "Rebuke me not, O sinner, in thy wrath, for ye shall be saved." Moreover, the content of his replies was entirely related to Biblical material.

I was awed by this patient's inordinate ability to speak this way so fluently; it was as though he had practiced this over a period of many years. During his first several days in the hospital, Paul showed no deviation from this behavior pattern: he continued to communicate exclusively in this manner and attempted to baptize everyone to whom he spoke.

Information provided by the patient's family was as one might anticipate. Paul was raised within a strong fundamentalist Protestant atmosphere and was always a very religious person, in the mechanical sense. He had always been a regular churchgoer and had considered the church an ultimate authority within his family. At no time in the past, however, had Paul acted in a bizarre manner or exhibited overt emotional symptoms. He was not known to have experienced any severe problems in his childhood, and his adolescence was characterized by achievement.

While attending high school, he was an active participant on the golf, tennis, and swimming teams and, during his senior year, was given an award for academic achievement. After being graduated from high school, he worked at some odd jobs until his marriage, when he began working for a construction company and attending college part-time.

Paul was placed on appropriate medications and after seven days showed a gratifying, but modest, improvement. He was now able to discuss some aspects of his problem, though he persisted in giving many of his answers to questions in the form of Biblical phrases, which were, of course, inappropriate to the questions and in the context of the hospital setting. When he was asked why he felt it was necessary to respond this way, he stated that he had committed the unpardonable sin, which he described as the "atrocity of the tongue."

Later it developed that he was referring to fellatio and cunnilingus, in which he and his wife had recently indulged. He expressed the feeling that God had recently made him aware that these acts were sinful and that, as a result, any of his subsequent children might be born with "afflictions." He went on to say that he was dead but would return with the second coming of Christ.

As the weeks progressed Paul was increasingly able to let go of his delusional thought patterns and began to speak coherently again. After a few weeks he was able to converse in a relatively normal fashion, with only an occasional reference to the Bible. At that time I discharged him from the hospital, with the agreement that he would return twice weekly for outpatient therapy. He left the hospital and was never heard from again.

The theme and variations of Paul's psychotic reaction were clearly of Biblical connotation. His escape from reality led him into a self-centered world of religious fantasy; it was as though his thought processes were being bombarded with heavenly messages.

One must question why religion was selected as a theme; why not some other subject?

The answer to this is complex and touches on some basic psychoanalytic theory. Because this is not a textbook of psychoanalysis, but merely a compendium of ideas and observations with a view toward prevention of such problems before they arise or can become severe, an abbreviated explanation will be presented here.

It is generally accepted by most psychiatrists that during a psychotic episode, material that is normally confined to the unconscious is allowed to rise to the surface and be expressed in the form of delusions and hallucinations. Also generally accepted is the theory that material stored in the unconscious mind has been collected throughout the person's life—possibly this collection process even starts in fetal life. (Any good textbook of psychoanalytic theory will explain this in detail.)

I would theorize—although it is perhaps an oversimplification—that a great deal of the Biblical material in Paul's delusions originated from his early childhood church memories via an erupting unconscious. His lifelong exposure to intense religious preachings provided the sheet music for a psychotic symphonette. I support this statement by pointing out again that Paul spoke "as though he had practiced this for a period of many years"; indeed he had.

This case history dramatically demonstrates the kinship of religion and mental illness in a patient who, cybernetically speaking, was like an erratic computer, programmed with the New Testament. This is not to say that religion caused this patient to have a schizophrenic reaction; but it would be difficult, even for an avid skeptic, to deny that religion had played a major part in the progression and maintenance of Paul's illness. There are elements in this case that are reminiscent of Angela and Luke.

As Paul attempted to unfold his own case history for me, it was noteworthy that he was quite upset over his "sin" of oral-genital sexuality. This concern had arisen from a well-ingrained matrix of religious mores. Had his upbringing allowed for generally more liberal sexual attitudes, Paul might have escaped at least one aspect of his problem. (I refer the reader to Axiom 3.)

This is not to say that there are religions that spell out approval of fellatio and cunnilingus; there are, however, other religions that propound fewer strictures about sexuality and therefore imply more flexible and liberal thinking on such matters.

The reason for this couple's participation in oral-genital

activity is not at issue here. Nor is it of any immediate importance to surmise symbolic meanings for these sexual practices (certainly such practices are commonplace in contemporary society). Of great import is the fact that, for reasons stated in Axiom 3, Paul had pathological feelings of guilt because he practiced these sexual rituals. His desire to baptize everyone in order to annihilate their sins seems to have been an attempt actually to deal with his own feelings of guilt, of self-sin. This desire to baptize was the central theme of his delusional system. It is therefore of great importance that the desire might have been avoided.

One probable criticism of my use of this case history might be that it is so very dramatic, uncommon, and thus not representative of other cases. While this case is dramatic, I can assure the reader that such criticism would seldom come from anyone with some experience working in a psychiatric hospital. Patients with variations of such delusions as illustrated by Paul are exceedingly common. In fact, they are ubiquitous—few large psychiatric units at a given time are without such a patient. To amplify the routineness of this case, I offer now some additional case histories and discussion.

Case History 4

Mary, thirty years old, was admitted to the hospital after becoming highly agitated and fearful while at home. She had been employed as a secretary in a very busy office and the stress at work recently had increased to a degree that she could not tolerate. Her past history was significant in that she had been hospitalized twice before with complaints of "depression."

At the time of her present hospitalization she was not

overtly depressed; rather, she was found to be in a state of elation and euphoria. She roamed about the psychiatric unit, soliciting the autographs of all the patients and staff members; she said she was compiling these for use in a movie she was to produce. She felt that the movie, in turn, would serve as a salvation for mankind. She tended to wander uninvited into other patients' rooms and became a general challenge for the nursing staff to handle.

She told me during an initial interview that she was Jesus Christ, the Virgin Mary, or possibly God. She went on to explain that, at various times, she was able to become any of these three figures. In addition, she felt that the nurses were conspiring against her because they knew about her special mission.

The patient was raised in a strict Catholic environment, which included regular church attendance, confession, and a parochial-school education. At age sixteen she had become pregnant, was not sure of the likely father, and at the suggestion of her mother, underwent a therapeutic abortion.

When I saw her in the hospital, she was married and had five children; her husband, also Catholic, was employed as an auto mechanic. During the lengthy hospitalization, Mary made numerous references to "her ultimate sin," which was the abortion that had been performed fourteen years earlier. At times she expressed the feeling that the abortion was not her fault, however, because she was indeed a virgin, or more specifically, the Virgin Mary.

With intensive individual psychotherapy and supportive medications, Mary showed a gradual improvement and was discharged from the hospital after three months. She was still incapable of returning to work, however, and barely managed her household.

Again I have presented an example of delusions arising from a Biblical context, delusions constructed in the patient's mind, using building blocks borrowed from childhood religious indoctrination. Guilt, apparently associated with the Catholic position on abortion, was more than Mary could deal with in a healthy way; she had to rationalize the guilt via a psychotic system of delusions (I am the Virgin Mary; therefore I am not responsible for this pregnancy; therefore I am not responsible for this abortion).

Most disturbing in this patient (and not seen in any previous examples) was the fact that she lost contact with her own identity. So profound was Mary's guilt that she could no longer deal with the reality of who she actually was. Much of the time, especially when frightened by something, she would assume the identity of Christ, God, or the Virgin. Unquestionably, the misidentity was directly related to her religious indoctrination, a fact made apparent by her choice of the Virgin most of the time.

As with Paul, Mary's psychotic episode was not actually triggered by religious problems: the stress at work seemed to be responsible. But like Paul, Mary was made more susceptible to stress by misguided religious beliefs.

Case History 5

Chris is a twenty-five-year-old unmarried Mormon who was referred to the psychiatric unit by his employer and with the permission of his parents. He was a part-time college student who worked in a doughnut shop and lived by himself in a studio apartment.

For the previous four or five days the patient had been in a state of mania: he was expending inordinate amounts of energy cleaning his apartment three or four times daily and disrupting everything at work. He would approach every customer and begin long monologues about rather intimate topics. Upon arriving on the psychiatric ward, he was seen to change his clothes three times within a half hour. He ran about the unit in a frenzy and spoke loudly, continuously, and for the most part incoherently to everyone he saw. He summarily alienated most of the other patients by entering rooms without knocking and rudely interrupting their conversations.

After one week his hospital room took on the appearance of a disaster area with bedclothing, linens, and personal articles strewn about the floor in the midst of half-eaten food. Only infrequently was anyone able to communicate effectively with Chris. During an interview, the patient told me that he was Jesus Christ and was communicating directly with God. He had recently had intercourse for the first time and felt guilty about this in light of his religious belief. He was certain, though, that God was going to forgive him and that he was ready to receive forgiveness.

He responded quite poorly to every treatment approach, and on the sixteenth day of his hospitalization he jumped out of a second-story window. Miraculously, he sustained only minor contusions. Prior to this, no indication of suicidal tendencies was even suggested.

The patient had an uncle who lived nearby and kindly gave us some background history. Chris was the eighth of ten children who grew up in a very pious Mormon family. He had always been a bright, ambitious boy with numerous hobbies and talents. He excelled in high school and was very active in his church; he had a burning ambition to become a Mormon missionary. It is common for young

Mormons to be encouraged in this direction, but for Chris it became an obsession. He had always respected his parents, but felt that he was an unexpected and thus unwanted child.

The first recollected innuendo of an emotional problem was the time when Chris, then thirteen, was participating in a school play. He was having great difficulty reconciling his Mormon religious beliefs with the Jewish beliefs he was to assume while play-acting. This marked the onset of what was to become a long series of wide mood swings. He was hospitalized during these periods on several occasions, and during those admissions, was always either profoundly depressed or highly elated and out of control.

In this current episode of illness he began to improve after two months and returned to his apartment and job.

Both of the preceding patients were psychotic; both had severe problems in delineating their identity; and both at one time or another assumed the identity of Christ.

It is common for psychotic patients to have grandiose delusions of identity; this is true in illnesses with a known organic cause (such as advanced syphilis) as well as in the schizophrenias and other psychoses. It is especially true in any emotional disturbance in which the patient is suspicious or paranoid, but it is not enough to say that Mary and Chris had delusions of grandeur. It is significant that their sources of identity emanated from the New Testament.

If one were to try through fantasy to consider grand objects of identification, many figures might come to mind: the President of the United States, Mao Tse-tung, famous movie stars, esteemed scientists, and noted historical figures. Though such delusional identifications are occasionally seen in the psychotic, they occur rather infrequently. Most commonly a patient will tend to identify with a religious figure, and usually that figure is Christ. I would venture to say with confidence that either Christ, the Virgin Mary, or God is incorporated into delusions and hallucinations in the overwhelming majority of psychotic patients who become grandiose.

It is common, as exemplified in Mary's delusions, that a patient may be confused even within the context of the delusion itself. She was not sure whether she was Jesus, the Virgin, or God; in fact, she changed her identity from day to day, but never departed from the holy theme. One would have to suspect the selection of such delusional identity figures to be a result of childhood religious indoctrination, for many of these patients were victims of overzealous church involvement when they were children.

These patients, after treatment and a return to reality, displayed an intense fear of God, which can be assumed to have been present prior to illness. Like Angela, they were victims of an enlarged conscience, inflated with religious mores and other teachings. They were also similarly endowed with inflated unconscious processes, which became conscious in the midst of a psychotic breakdown.

To explain this further, I will again touch briefly on some basic psychoanalytic theory. It is generally accepted that the material or memories of the unconscious mind are assimilated throughout life. Much of this material was acquired during childhood and stored in the unconscious for definite reasons. According to psychoanalysts, the child (and the adult, for that matter) incorporates difficult-to-deal-with concepts or thoughts into the unconscious in order to avoid dealing with them on the conscious level.

As a result of this process, the difficult-to-deal-with concept is blotted out of awareness and apparently "forgotten." The mechanism by which this is done is called repression, which differs from forgetting: in repression the thought is not cast away, but is merely placed in storage in the unconscious. Later in life these thoughts, though unconscious, can give rise to anxiety, therefore causing neurotic problems; or they may emerge in toto from the unconscious in the form of a psychotic reaction. Again, this is greatly simplifying a pillar of psychoanalytic theory, but it sets the stage for my next point.

If one were to accept at face value most of the teachings and preachings emanating from the pulpit and Bible, one would have to become a paragon of virtue. This is especially true for the more dogmatic and fundamentalist churches, because in these settings the moralizing can be repetitive, intense, and supported with great—even mortal —fear.

If the child who is exposed to all this is hearing the same messages at home, and/or if he tends to be quite naïve and suggestible, the unconscious storage locker may be put to the ultimate test. He soon finds that he is unable to live up to his religious authority to the letter and finds it necessary to repress whatever he cannot handle. The more he must live up to satisfying the expectations set up by his church, the more he must repress and the more strained his unconscious will become.

I suggest that this represents much of the dilemma for the patients I have discussed thus far. Indeed, it would take an exceptionally rare person who might be capable of living up to the dictates of dogmatic fundamentalist beliefs.

Churches often provide one side of a destructive dichotomy, the other side being provided by a person's natural impulses. And this recalls another patient I was treating for a psychotic reaction.

The amount of religious exposure she received as a child

was phenomenal. Again and again over the years she was bitterly warned by her preachers of the evils of dancing, swearing, drinking, and lovemaking. She abided by all these teachings with remarkable self-control until she was eighteen, when she had a sexual affair. Her intense feelings of guilt about this affair led her into a psychotic reaction.

Here there was a dichotomy between her intense religious teachings on one side and her biological sexual drives on the other. Her mind was unable to reconcile this highly competitive paradox in a healthy manner and so the result was devastating. Her unconscious mind, already overburdened with such dichotomies collected over many years, was unable to deal with biological impulses when these powerfully manifested themselves upon her reaching maturity. Because it could no longer bear the strain, the unconscious became conscious and the patient became psychotic. Analogies of this case history to the previous ones are apparent—for example, Paul's guilt over oral-genital sexual practices.

The identification with Christ is so often an integral part of a psychotic reaction because, in my opinion, Christ and what he represents to various people is closely associated with what makes a person vulnerable to psychosis in the first place. Early childhood assimilation of religious teachings and values has a tendency to form a weak spot, making some persons especially vulnerable to mental illness. These events may all occur to a lesser degree, giving rise to neurotic problems rather than to the more profound psychotic disturbances. The former, though not as easily demonstrated, occurs with much greater frequency.

To demonstrate this phenomenon, I have purposely chosen case histories of psychotic patients. First of all, this allows me to demonstrate how very dangerous religious interplay can be on a person's thinking processes: in the psychotic the effect is almost malignant. Another reason is that because the unconscious mind of the psychotic surfaces quite readily, conclusions can be drawn from tangible observations. In the neurotic the unconscious mind is protected from close examination by a multitude of defense mechanisms. It is therefore more difficult to relate causes and effects in the less severely ill (but more commonly seen) patients.

It is one thing for a surgeon carefully to examine the X-rays of a patient with a suspected ulcer, but it is quite another matter when, at the operating table, he can look directly at the lesion and even touch it. So it is with the examination of the unconscious in the neurotic versus the psychotic.

The religious theme and variations of so many psychotic reactions cannot occur merely by happenstance; there is without question a complex interplay between religion and the state of one's mental pathology.

Thus far I have not quantified or given statistics on the occurrence rate of "psychotoreligious" reactions (psychotic illnesses with a religious flavor). I am not sure that statistics would be helpful, or even possible, because of the subjectivity in determining which cases are and are not intimately involved with religion. I can cite some specifics, however, that will lend support to the fact that such occurrences are plentiful.

While recently associated with a mental health unit that consisted of only forty beds, I had occasion to deal directly and indirectly with most of the patients. Though there was a seasonal fluctuation, the daily inpatient census usually varied between thirty and thirty-eight patients. I would grossly estimate that at any given time no more than half of these patients were psychotic; the remainder could be classified as having neurotic or sociopathic problems.

I vividly recall that at one time there were three patients on the ward who simultaneously had delusions that they were Jesus Christ. There may have been twenty or so psychotic patients present at that point; thus one could say that 15 percent of them were having a "psychotoreligious" reaction. One must also remember that I have spoken only of those patients who had grandiose delusions of being Christ. Experience tells me that there were at least again that number of patients whose illnesses were intimately related, though not so dramatically, to their religious upbringings.

I would grant to critics that this situation was somewhat exceptional, but I would maintain nevertheless that it was not a remote coincidence. More often than not, among this changing population of approximately twenty patients, there is at least one who at some point in his illness thinks that he is Christ. More significantly, there are always, to my knowledge, several patients in that small population whose symptoms have a religious basis.

Although it is noteworthy that most of these patients at my particular hospital, in my particular area of the country, are of Christian heritage, this does not mean to imply that Jewish people have a kind of immunity against a religious interplay in severe mental illnesses. A colleague shared with me his experience with a Jewish man who was being treated for a psychotic illness. The man insisted that he was one of the great rabbinical scholars of all time.

I would not want to mislead the reader into thinking that religious delusions and hallucinations always indicate a religious foundation within a person's illness; this is certainly not the case. Delusional misidentifications may at times simply incorporate a figure greatly admired by the patient.

If I were to see a psychotic musician who told me that he was Mozart, I certainly would not implicate the latter's musical compositions as a foundation for the illness. It is significant, though, how very seldom nonreligious misidentifications are utilized by the severely ill.

In addition, before I conclude that religion has formed part of the foundation of a person's illness, I take into consideration not only delusions and hallucinations, but a background history, which is of even greater import. But when delusions of such religious flavor occur, there is no question that one commonly finds the religious background intricately woven into the evolution of the illness.

5

Religion and Life Situations

A person need not be psychotic or even prepsychotic to feel the potentially adverse effects of his religion. In this chapter I will discuss life situations that affect people in general, people who may never feel the need of a psychiatrist's consultation, but who are nevertheless unhappy or in a dilemma.

In all the various accepted definitions of what constitutes mental health, happiness (in the absence of exogenous sorrowful situations) is an integral requirement. Though much of the time I will discuss people who are not under treatment for specific neurotic or psychotic problems, I will not be departing from the general theme of mental health. As far as I am concerned, a person placed in a continuing situation promoting unhappiness cannot be enjoying his ultimate capacity for being mentally healthy. I will be discussing microcosms of American society and the impact of religious customs and beliefs on those microcosms.

It is not necessary for a person to be a believer in religion to feel its effects. If his family, his community, his employer, and others around him practice and believe, this can suffice to set the stage for significant conflicts. Depending upon the intensity and timing of religious indoctrination in a person's life, a template (or stencil) is formed, usually in childhood, that will dictate various rules of living as time goes by. This mold, incidentally, may be good for those people who find it difficult to make basic decisions and develop a personal philosophy in life.

Certainly some church-dictated rules and concepts can be usefully applied; few would argue with the commandments against killing and stealing. A vast number of other rules, however, vary in their effects from harmless to useless to dangerous. For example, I look at the Jewish custom of keeping a kosher home as useless, while I see the Catholic attitude toward contraception as dangerous.

Because a sacred aura tends to surround these dictates, they are unlikely to be challenged even by religious practitioners who are intelligent and pragmatic in other matters. Once a rule or commandment is handed down, it tends to endure long after it can still be looked upon as serving a purpose. When the point of obsolescence is reached, the rule is seldom cast off. Rather, it is reexplained or rationalized to update it or give it new meaning. If it becomes impossible to reexplain or rationalize such a rule, it can still be salvaged in the name of tradition and thereby lose any meaning it might have had initially.

For example, the Jewish practice of keeping a kosher home is thought by most people (including Jewish people) to have orginated as a health precaution against the parasitic disease trichinosis, which is harbored by pigs. This would have been of great meaning not only centuries ago, but even today, when trichinosis is still occasionally seen in people who have eaten infected and improperly cooked pork. This is presumptuous thinking, however, in the context of what the Old Testament actually says; the practice of keeping a kosher home did not start as a health precaution. It began, rather, as a means of isolating an identity for the Jewish people.

I do not question the validity of this intention. I merely point out that this custom is being followed by a multitude of Jewish people for the "wrong" reason.

With the same retrospective thinking, many Jewish physicians today claim that the ritual of circumcision began as a prophylaxis against certain diseases of the penis (it has been shown recently that circumsised penises have a lesser chance of developing malignant tumors). But circumcision also began as a custom to promote Jewish identity. Many physicians today question the medical justification for the continuation of this routine procedure; some, in fact, feel that it should not be done so that the foreskin could be used at a later date, should there be a need for skin grafting.

Even on the rare occasion when a church recalls or alters a rule, one finds the parishioners or congregation often unwilling to give it up. Many restaurants and cafeterias continue offering Friday fish specials, possibly because of popular demand. In the hospital with which I am associated I always regret the Friday fish-stick entrée, which seems to have become a monotonous ritual with the dietary department. Keeping a kosher home and avoiding meat on certain calendar days are trivial matters, though, when compared with much more profound dictates.

The Catholic Church seems to be in the very slow process of changing its stance on matters such as divorce. Thus far its attitude has placed countless patients in the offices of psychiatrists and on the couches of analysts. An even greater number of people have been plagued by the dilemma of living with a divorce decree without seeking professional counseling.

Obviously, many people seek help for a variety of conflicts arising from their marital situations, and much of the time the problems can be resolved and the marriage bond reinforced. Frequently, on the other hand, when the situation has been looked into and thoroughly reconsidered, only one alternative remains: separation and divorce; these become the only realistic resolutions of the conflict. For the believing Catholic this alternative has not been available before, and as a result numerous miserable marriages were salvaged and maintained in vain. It is of little consolation to these victims that the Church is beginning to reconsider its attitude and redefine its dicta.

I recall, with feelings of sympathy, the recent news story of an eighty-year-old Italian gentleman who was now (with the permission of the Church) filing for divorce to end a lifelong empty marriage. The story was presented for its comedy value, which to me was an absurd, disdainful paradox. For many people changes in rules come too late, if at all.

The Church forgets that, like itself, people change lifelong patterns of thinking only with some reluctance and pain. Just as many Catholics will continue to insist on Friday fish or macaroni with cheese, they will continue to have difficulty approaching divorce with objectivity. Moreover, even a Catholic seeking divorce with the blessing of his Church will for some time to come have difficulty accepting this freedom without feelings of guilt. If an Orthodox Jew (who, according to orthodoxy, has kept a kosher home throughout his life) decides to convert to Reform Judaism (where the keeping of a kosher home is not such a major issue), the chances are he could only attempt eating bacon with some hesitation and guilt.

As to therapeutic abortion, it is obvious from the trend of liberalizing laws being passed by state legislatures that our population is reconsidering all aspects of this rather simple operative procedure. The arguments on both sides of this issue have frequently been overly emotional and ridiculous. Few people are advocating abortion as a desirable method of birth control; certainly there are simpler, less expensive, and more efficacious means of controlling the population explosion. I prefer to think of abortion in many instances as a means not of controlling population, but, rather, of preventing emotional difficulties for parents and children.

First, it is necessary to examine the feelings and attitudes of an expectant mother who is seeking an abortion. I am most concerned with her attitude toward the fetus, regardless of the stage of gestation; it is certainly fair to say that, at best, her attitude toward the fetus is one of ambivalence and that, most probably, it is more negative than positive. Certainly the sum total of her feelings is that she does not want the baby.

It is safe to assume that this attitude may continue with the birth and growing up of that child, who will fall victim to the atmosphere of parental ambivalence or indifference. The mother may even develop a resentful attitude toward the child from the outset and make his healthy emotional growth an impossibility. In cases in which the biological father refuses to become the legal father, the mother may displace her feelings of hate for the man onto the child, who is, after all, a part of him. And so, at the very worst, the child often becomes the scapegoat for an angry mother who hates men; if the child should be a male, his dilemma may be even worse.

With the advent of women's liberation movements it is becoming more accepted (and even a status-laden fad) for a woman to bear and raise children on her own. This does not alter the above psychodynamic situation that can result in tragedy for the child and feelings of guilt for the mother. Women's lib sadly misses the boat by making it entirely an issue of equality and other impossible-to-define concepts.

In many states without updated abortion laws the operation can be performed legally only when "the life of the mother is in danger" if the pregnancy continues. Because there is seldom an ironclad medical indication for the abortion, the gynecologist will usually call upon a colleague, the psychiatrist, to provide the indication. The patient is thus subjected to an unneeded psychiatric evaluation, to the tune of thirty to a hundred dollars, so that the psychiatrist can call upon his creative resources to provide a legal justification for the operative procedure.

The Catholic Church has every intention of maintaining this absurdity via its lobbying to maintain archaic state laws in states not yet enlightened. In doing so, the Church is force-feeding mores not only to its own people, but to the general population as well.

So much for the obvious legal issue. What about the psychiatric implications of an abortion involving a Catholic patient, a Catholic psychiatrist, and a Catholic gynecologist? What about the issue, often raised by the Catholic antiabortionists, regarding the maternal mental scar after the abortion?

First of all, it is exceedingly rare for patients to retain significant residual emotional problems following an abortion. Most experienced gynecologists, who have collectively performed thousands of abortions, will attest to this. The "mental scar" so often talked about, is in effect usually a myth; it is seldom a problem for the overwhelming majority of patients. On the infrequent occasion when residual emotional problems do occur, they can often be traced to the person's religious mores. Experience tells me that those patients having difficulty accepting the experience are Catholic more often than can be explained as chance.

Now it becomes apparent that if the Church cannot discourage a member from undergoing an abortion, it will punish her afterward for having had it. This became an obvious component of Mary's illness (a dramatic but clearcut example). Though usually not this obviously expressed, feelings of post-abortion guilt in Catholic women are often present to a bothersome degree.

The Church, then, has its followers in a double bind on the abortion issue: it has defined the "crime" (by equating abortion with murder) and prescribed the punishment (guilt). It is an unfortunate dilemma of being "damned if you do and damned if you don't."

Especially disturbing to me, as a physician, is the attitude of many Catholic gynecologists and especially Catholic psychiatrists on this issue. For many of them delineation of a philosophy on a subject falling within their area of expertise becomes stifled and interrupted by a Catholic "filter effect" and "fail-safe" (see Chapter 2). Many of these physicians will refuse even to discuss the abortion issue with colleagues or will become emotionally overheated if such discussion does take place.

It is well known and therefore not unexpected that many Catholic gynecologists refuse to perform the procedure purely on religious grounds, regardless of the patient's reason for wanting it. As much as I deplore this fixated stance, I must respect a gynecologist's right to refuse doing a procedure that he deplores. However, I cannot accept the attitude of psychiatrists who automatically reject abortion on religious grounds.

There is a major distinction here: the psychiatrist is acting as a middleman who is selling Catholic dicta to his unfortunate patient. He is forcing the patient to adopt his system of mores or, in actuality, his Church's system of mores. The gynecologist is merely standing true to his own mores and not necessarily attempting to force this onto his patient.

I do not intend to enter deeply into the pro-and-con arguments of abortion; in the media this debate has become a study in clichés and futility. I will take the liberty, however, of amplifying some important points. The pregnant woman who harbors feelings of ambivalence toward her unborn child can inflict inordinate emotional damage on that child. In fact, she will often do so. If that woman undergoes an abortion, her chances for sustaining emotional difficulties are relatively slight. It thus seems unfortunate that many Catholic psychiatrists refuse to probe open-mindedly into this matter with any patient, under any circumstances. The same psychiatrists would most probably shy away from such stereotyped thinking on nonreligious matters.

It is apparent that the Catholic girl with an unwanted pregnancy can resort to only two alternatives: she can rear the child or give him up for adoption. Adoption agencies— many with religious affiliations—are reporting baby shortages and therefore encourage the latter alternative over abortion. It is apparent, then, that many people (with a variety of motivations) are anxious to help a mother get rid of an unwanted baby. Though their intentions are good for the most part, they seem to take everyone into consideration except the mother herself.

What they all seem to forget is that during a nine-month pregnancy, this woman has made a real investment, physically and emotionally. While the investment is certainly there, it falls short of turning this biological mother into an emotionally gratifying mother. But it is enough to set the stage for a depressive reaction, especially at the time of birth.

The mother who gives up a child for adoption goes through a stage of mourning, much the same as if a loved one had died. In many cases this is prolonged and the mother will continue to fantasize in vain and ask herself a flood of troubling questions: What does the baby look like? Is the baby happy? and so on. Therefore, the mother's alternative of giving away the unwanted baby can be just as bad as keeping the unwanted baby. The latter, as I have said, is even worse because the baby might suffer the plight of having an ambivalent mother.

Many Catholic psychiatrists, guided by the Church rather than their years of professional training, choose to remain oblivious to these considerations and are therefore relatively impotent in conferring with mothers who are trying to work out a solution to the very common conflict of an unwanted pregnancy.

In Chapter 2 I offered some observations on the growing up of the Jewish child in a Christian society, with special attention to the trials of Christmastime. Because most Jewish adolescents go to college to study, college is a good place to study them. The Jewish college fraternity (a dying institution) provides a microcosm for numerous observations. I would like to discuss some of my observations on general attitudes, dating customs, and marital patterns. I draw on experiences from two large university campuses and two different fraternities.

Many Jewish high-school graduates have in the past had to deal with a severe conflict on arriving at a college campus. The conflict started long before the bar mitzvah and emanates from parental attitudes. Since before World War II American Jews have attempted in many ways to become assimilated into their surrounding society. Concomitantly, they have tried to inculcate their children with a strong sense of being Jewish. The child has thus sorted his way through a series of double messages in order to arrive at adolescence. He has also found it necessary to bow for many years to the numerous needs of a Jewish mother, who is often a very formidable entity.

His arrival on campus marks an often badly needed milestone of social freedom and he frequently becomes preoccupied with the thought that his parents have been hypocrites about religious beliefs, dating restrictions, etc. Throughout the high-school dating period he observed his parents' casual attendance at the synagogue, typically three times a year. Yet he was essentially required to be socially Jewish himself, by exclusively dating Jewish girls. A rebellion directed at the parents (alluded to in Chapter 2) now manifests itself in one of two forms.

Occasionally and infrequently, the young college student increases his interest and participation in Judaism. He may begin compulsive attendance at Friday night services, even at the expense of having a date that evening. He may increasingly participate in organized, Jewish, collegiate activity. A small minority of these adolescents even return to orthodox customs—for example, keeping the kosher laws; sometimes indulgence to the point of religious fanaticism will occur.

This pattern may continue into marriage and thus create an irony within the family constellation: when Mother and Dad come to visit, they must now respect a newly religious atmosphere in their son's or daughter's household. Fortunately, though often founded on rebellion, this backlash of religious enlightenment is harmless and perhaps even enriching for the participant.

Another form of rebellion is more common and sometimes devastating. It occurs not only on an individual level, but on the group or fraternity level. Many of these students are frankly sick of Judaism. They would prefer to deny it at this point, and become assimilated into the general college community. But assimilation does not come automatically because of rush week. Though the tide is turning in view of the popularity of the civil rights issue, many college fraternities will not accept Jews in membership—which is why "Jewish" fraternities were conceived in the first place.

Since the young student realizes now that he will have to "work at it" to attain general acceptance, he settles for a Jewish fraternity and wrestles with the problem there from within. He is delighted to discover that his fraternity brothers are wrestling with the same problem of assimilation and acceptance; therefore, the effort becomes a group one. Finally, it becomes an unwritten group policy that denial or belittlement of religion shall define proper etiquette. The solemn prayer at mealtime is replaced by "Rub-a-dub-dub, thanks for the grub." Dating of Jewish girls is frowned upon and parties with Jewish sororities are discouraged.

The cycle most commonly culminates in the selection of a non-Jewish marital partner. The latter represents the finale in the separation from (and rebellion against) the parent. It is at this point that devastating consequences often surface. Many times the family constellation is ripped apart, often beginning with the parents' refusal to attend the wedding ceremony. The young man or woman is getting married in spite of his parents' wishes, and this represents only the beginning of the problem, from a psychiatric viewpoint.

Arising from this very common dilemma are feelings of guilt for the parents and the son or daughter. From that point on the parents will ruminate about "Where did I go wrong?" "What could I have done to avoid all this?" and so on. What they overlook is that they, through their double messages to their children, have been greatly responsible. Even after laying the groundwork years earlier, they continue to refuse to accept the outcome. The guilt feelings of the son or daughter may be distressing and continuing. Hardly a person exists who lacks a great desire to win the approval of his parents; for many children in this current dilemma the approval will not be forthcoming, and a multitude of guilty feelings will take its place. In later life this will often be converted into anxiety, depression, or renewed and increased guilt, especially when a guilt-inducing parent dies.

Here, as in other examples, it was the misuse of religion that led to problems. The son or daughter is found to be using religion as an effective weapon for rebelling against (and punishing) his parents. He finds it an appropriate weapon because it is the same weapon they used to punish him in the years prior to college. When this weapon is used, no one wins.

Axiom 6: **Religious dictates during youth can place people later in irreversible, unresolvable dilemmas, leading to permanent unhappiness.**

I will amplify this axiom, hinted at previously, with another case history.

Case History 6

John and Sarah were a Catholic couple who had been married sixteen years when I first saw them. I initially interviewed John at the request of a gastroenterologist who had been treating him for a chronic peptic ulcer. It seems that

John was aggravating his ulcer with increased alcoholic intake. It was apparent after several interviews that the drinking was his response to many situational problems involving the whole family.

During their sixteen years of marriage the couple regretfully gave birth to eleven children who varied now in age from three to fifteen. Though they never desired a family larger than four, birth-control methods had been avoided until after the birth of their youngest. At that time Sarah's gynecologist strongly advised against further pregnancies. In light of the family situation, the couple was angry at the Church and felt that it was to blame for their oversized family. They in effect disowned the Church and ceased going to mass shortly after the birth of their eleventh.

John earned $9600 annually in a computer-programming job; Sarah earned about half that amount as a secretary and paid half of her salary to babysitters. The couple was finding that their combined income was not even enough to keep up with the minimum credit-card payments they owed. Now, with the deterioration of John's health, spiraling financial crises, and an unmanageable family, the situation for Sarah was becoming more critical.

For a while the couple was treated together in a group therapy setting, and it was becoming apparent that they were turning on each other under the general strain of their life situation. John found his solution by taking a large overdose of sleeping pills and was dead soon after arriving at an outlying hospital. Sarah became acutely depressed and even less capable of running the family than before. She chose to go on welfare and send her two youngest children to foster homes.

This tragedy involved two people who were, for the most part, without profound mental problems until certain burdening life situations became intolerable. Many theorize that everyone has a breaking point, but, fortunately, most of us will never know what that point is. Technically, in applying accepted theory to this case, one could surmise that John's suicide was a symbolic act of murdering his wife, who had, in effect, burdened him with such an adverse life situation —that is, more children than he could support. Then again, it may have represented a symbolic act of killing his children, the Church, or the Pope. Or, to be less theoretical for a moment, maybe he just plain wanted out.

I am less interested here in academic interpretations than I am in the factors that led up to the situation. It is apparent that the same church that had dictated dietary and other restrictions in this man's way of living had also indirectly prescribed to him the size of his family. In turn, family size was both directly and indirectly the major force providing what became the secondary motives for suicide—for example, financial crises and household turmoil.

Such situations are irreversible. If the Church were to change its stand today dramatically on the birth-control issue, the news would be greeted as an anticlimax for those many families and entire countries afflicted with the malignancy of overpopulation.

The Church seems to be committed to unilateral responsibility on the birth-control issue: it prescribes the taboo but ignores the consequences. In this respect Catholicism seems to be posing a threat, not just to Catholics and predominately Catholic countries, but to mankind in general. The increasing enlightenment of people on this issue makes it unnecessary to belabor the point.

As before, the examples used in this chapter were chosen only because they serve as good illustrations. Certainly, Catholics and Jews do not have a monopoly on such problems any more than the fundamentalist Protestants hold a monopoly on psychosis (see Chapter 4). Yet the examples I have cited are exceedingly common within the Jewish and Catholic communities, although suicide is fortunately not often chosen by Catholics as an attempt to resolve the conflict.

I find it difficult to discuss religion's interplay with life situations without touching on a discussion of sexual mores. In some ways it appears that our society has entered a renaissance of sexual interest and open-mindedness, as indicated by the trends of the media: Underground pornographic movies have moved into respectable theaters, making respectable sums of money; both men's and women's magazines have been preoccupied for some time with the subject. I look at this not as an indication of enlightened thinking but, rather, as voyeuristic thrill-seeking, an offshoot of our religiously founded moral structure.

It is not that people have suddenly become more open; but it has become more socially acceptable to window-peek and window-display. Probably since they began, the religions of the world have been analyzing, defining, and controlling sexual drives and activities. Few clergymen get through a year of preaching without at some point getting caught up in the subject. I am concerned with a more subtle attitude conveyed by churches. Though not explicit, it is continually implied.

For example, the Catholic Church considers it a virtue for its nuns and priests to abstain from sexual activity. Regardless of their reason for this policy, abstinence is generally equated with goodness; the logical converse of this would be that sexual activity is not good, but bad. This concept is glaringly apparent at the very heart of Christianity: Mary, a virgin, gave birth to Jesus.

I have often asked myself why the Bible's authors found it so necessary to portray her as a virgin. Did they not anticipate that belief in this concept might someday be difficult? So important is Mary's virginity that she is in fact referred to as "The Virgin." And so, at the very foundation of Christianity, virginity is equated with saintliness, making it difficult for most modern Christians to be saintly.

From the start, then, religions got snagged on sex and the suggestion that sex is bad continues to be perpetuated. The young child is indirectly taught long before puberty that sex, though not bad, is certainly not virtuous except as a means to an end—procreation.

This Christian ethic permeates our society and affects everyone: Christian, non-Christian, and atheist. It carries this impact because it has found its way into the very laws and etiquette by which all must live. It shows up clinically in vast numbers of cases of impotence and frigidity, which usually involve people who learned as children that sex is dirty and not to be enjoyed (I refer the reader to the latest writings of Dr. William H. Masters and Mrs. Virginia Johnson).

It is often easy for the clinician to understand through the patient's history why he or she is impotent or frigid, but it is quite a different matter to treat these people successfully. The sex-is-tainted attitude becomes deeply entrenched, and though the patient may see the light on an intellectual level, he finds it difficult to undo the problem emotionally and physiologically.

As a result, then, of the American-Christian religious ethic, sex is not yet looked upon as a biological drive, a component of love, or a need; rather, it is looked upon in other ways. Many see it as something to be sacrificed in the name of God or martyrdom (it seems ironic that God would endow someone with something he is not supposed to use). Others see sex as a commodity to be bought and sold. Still others look at sex "through the window" as a novelty or as forbidden fruit. The millionaires of the pornography business have modern religion to thank for their buying market; no one would pay a penny for an apple that was otherwise free (see Genesis).

6

How Sacred Is Religion?

Religion as a Commodity

Earlier I referred to religion as a commodity. I find this approach a necessity that facilitates a more objective and scientific viewpoint. But I quite recognize that religion is only a semitangible, and I do not claim to have carried out an extensive scientific investigation. Extensive statistics to support my conclusions simply are not available. This book is merely based on observation and what I believe to be a series of valid conclusions or hypotheses.

Looking at religion as a commodity allows the observer to be less subjective, and this is important. He must make an attempt to set aside his own religious beliefs, for if one studies another's religion only vis-à-vis his own, he can make valid conclusions only about similarities and differences. If he takes this approach and arrives at conclusions about mental illness, he is a chauvinist.

I have tried at all costs to avoid such a label. To initiate an effective study of this kind, one must be able to put aside religious feelings of allegiance and sacredness, if these feelings existed at the outset. This is why I look at religion here as an entity, as something a person can acquire or discard.

It is hoped that the use of the commodity metaphor allows us to look at the subject with candor, rather than with emotion and conviction; it is not an attempt to be facetious. And I will continue the liberal use of analogies, not because this is an ironclad method of argumentation, but for the sake of clarity.

A Seller's Market

Let us imagine, for the moment, a giant edifice. Within, there is a shopping center specializing in the sale of religion. There are hundreds of booths, each manned by a salesman wearing his company uniform.

Let us assume that each salesman is a clergyman, representing a national and sometimes international sales organization; each of these retailers appears eager to welcome you into his religion and in most cases into the local church franchise that represents it (he may actually be more or less eager, depending upon your color and nationality).

The salesmen make liberal use of gimmicks to persuade the perspective buyer. Some offer plush theaters designed for high-cost praying: others offer more modest structures with neon signs. Still others offer salvation and bingo— these salesmen tend to be more of the high-pressure variety and can be heard all night on AM and FM from their own radio stations. Some salesmen go door to door or use the United States mailman as their vehicle. On Sunday mornings they strive for equal television time, competing only with an infrequent press show or football rerun.

All of these salesmen seem to be representing one of three home offices: the Protestant, Catholic, and Jewish, in order of size (this is an American shopping center and imports are unwelcome).

This all might sound quite absurd, for it is apparent that

no such shopping center actually exists; if one did, it could not stay in business for very long because most people do not buy (that is, choose) their religion, they inherit it. It is seldom that a child spontaneously selects a religion other than that of his parents. In most cases it would not be allowed if he did try, much in the same way that his parents dictate dietary requirements: "Drink your milk, Johnnie. Mommy and Daddy know what's best for you."

People who eventually trade in old faithful and purchase (convert to) another religion usually co so only super-ficially. Almost invariably the person who "converts" is really just inheriting another religion, but this time from and for a spouse instead of the parents. In a way this is tragic when one considers how seriously people take their faith and what an important role their religion might play in their life.

I contend that most people take more care in selecting dog food and motor oil than their religion. Any one of these people would be appalled if you were to suggest to him that he use the same kind of motor oil in his new car that his father used in his 1948 DeSoto. Would it be absurd to consider that this man (who has passively bought father's faith) was any less different from his father than his car is from his father's car? I think not. And so it is apparent that, most of the time, a person declines to seek out a religion more suitable than his own, even if it should be causing him hardships (see Chapter 5). How presumptuous it is for people to assume that the effort of such a selection would be fruitless!

The Immortal Sacred Cow

It is precisely because the consumer does not look at religion as a commodity that it remains immune to much deserved criticism. People think of religion as sacred and even mystical, and therefore shy away from analyzing it. This is why religious beliefs and policies are only infrequently altered or updated.

Religion can be compared to a course taken in school. Certainly it is learned partially in the classroom; even a religious matriculation process occurs in many forms. If we make this comparison, the Bible takes the role of a textbook. Nobody would advocate the use of a 1924 edition chemistry text for use in a modern chemistry class—too much has been learned about chemistry since then. In the same way, much has been learned about sociology, philosophy, and psychology in the past several thousand years; nevertheless, the Bible (which has much to say about these subjects) is used as an authority and seldom revised.

I am always amazed when I hear someone discuss the "miracle" of how timeless the Bible is and how it is as meaningful today as it was when it was written. This is somewhat akin to one's amazement over the "accuracy" of astrology. The Bible has wielded such strong authority that few ever give consideration to updating or discarding it. Instead, an alternate and potentially dangerous course of action is taken.

The clergymen and associated scholars reinterpret the old passages in an attempt to apply them to modern times. Eventually they are reinterpreting their own interpretations and injecting into them their own personal biases. And so the Bible is reread backward, forward, upside down, and inside out, according to the whim of those select few who are in a position to do so. If a clergyman wants to tell his congregation that strobe lights at rock concerts are sinful, he can probably do so and use the Bible as an authority to support him.

As this whole process is allowed to grow, the clergyman

himself, not the Bible, can become the sacred cow with God-given authority. The Bible, then, is really used not as an authority, but as a vehicle with which a man can promote his own prejudices.

There is a point at which religion and psychology overlap, and this is the point that concerns me most. The Bible was written long before anyone knew anything about modern psychology and the psychosexual developmental process. Even if its writers' intentions were of the best, they could not have taken these important factors into consideration. Yet when it comes to the issue of morals and/or commandments, the Bible and its interpreters have much to say. In fact, they seem preoccupied by this. It is here that religion and psychology overlap and often meet head-on.

The clergyman is given Biblical power of attorney, by virtue of position, and is allowed, via interpretations, to inflict his own mores on the congregation. If he has neurotic conflicts, he may be guided by them in writing his sermons. If the preacher hates women and shies away from sexual gratifications, he may find it self-helpful and convenient to stress the evils of sex to his congregation. He thereby justifies his own hangups and cruelly overlooks the fact that his congregation may have sexual drives.

Many case histories come to mind. I know of one girl who at the age of sixteen was greatly troubled by her priest. He was encouraging her to become a nun. When she indicated that she had no such interest, he began to dwell on sexual mores. He did this to the absurd degree of discouraging her from using makeup or listening to rock-and-roll (this was several years ago); he said they were "erotic."

I think this priest must have had profound personal sexual conflicts and was trying to resolve them vicariously through this most unfortunate girl. I am convinced from my own associations with the clergy that people often gravitate toward a religious career as an attempt to resolve just such conflicts.

The Clergyman as a Psychotherapist

Not only does the Bible have much to say indirectly about psychology, but clergymen practice a great deal of psychotherapy. Where the parishioner (patient) with emotional problems is concerned, the domains of the clergyman and the psychiatrist overlap. Though the latter uses a wide variety of diagnostic and treatment approaches to help his patients, he spends the greatest amount of time in a dialogue with the patient. The clergyman similarly spends most of his time talking with his parishioners, either from the pulpit or on a one-to-one basis in counseling, confession, and various other settings.

All psychiatrists are aware that during that dialogue called psychotherapy, a patient may improve or worsen, depending upon many variables; psychotherapy can be a destructive process. Other likenesses between the clergyman and psychiatrist also exist and are of importance. Patients (parishioners) look upon their psychiatrists and clergymen as figures of authority whose word or advice is apt to command a great deal of respect and consequent response. Moreover, clergymen spend significant amounts of their time making hospital rounds like psychiatrists and other physicians. The overlapping domain of these professionals becomes even more evident today with the establishment of church counseling services, frequently staffed by the clergy.

Obviously a lot of clergymen practice a lot of "psychotherapy," and because there is an acute national shortage of mental health personnel, they could potentially fill a vital role. In further evaluating these clergy-therapists who are an integral part of the religious commodity, consideration must be given to their qualifications. This brings to mind the question of quality control in the ordination of the clergy, for if these people are to represent authority and practice psychotherapy, something should be known of their educational background.

The time spent on educating a clergyman varies from almost none to considerable. In many religious sects becoming a member of the clergy involves many years of education and sacrifice, comparable to any other profession such as law or medicine. This is certainly found to be the case in becoming a Catholic priest, a rabbi, or a minister in many of the Protestant faiths. In some of the more fundamentalist faiths, however, "education" is provided by diploma mills. They issue a "license to practice" just as do some schools of medical quackery that after a year or two license "practitioners" to collect fees for beating on your back.

As to training in psychology, some clergymen hold impressive credentials, others have none. Many hold various degrees in behavioral science; some have a Ph.D.; others have enrolled in medical schools and gone on to become psychiatrists. I am most concerned with the lack of qualifications of those who have had little or no formal training in this area. A lack of sophisticated insight (on the part of the clergyman-therapist) in counseling a parishioner (patient) can be replaced by religious moralizing, personal opinion (prejudice), or just plain bad advice.

I am not simply speaking, for example, of a rabbi talking man-to-man with a member of his congregation regarding personal problems, because in effect the voice coming from the pulpit can be compared to psychotherapy or, specifically, group therapy. The only difference is that the congregational setting is a more structured activity: the clergyman reads a formal sermon and leads the responsive reading to which the congregation formally replies. Even though this is predetermined, the authority figure on the pulpit commands a considerable amount of respect and the parishioner may therefore try to emulate him. This is often, though not always, a mechanism used by experienced therapists—that is, the therapist may attempt to act as a model for the group. Consequently, I choose to think of any religious service as a potential group therapy session, at least to some extent.

All of these comparisons, if the reader accepts them as valid, open the way for much potential good and also for possible tragedy. It is very important to remember that every congregation has members who are enjoying various degrees of mental health. Depending upon a person's commitment to his religious affiliation, the clergyman may wield considerable influence on the person's approach to life conflicts.

How does a Catholic priest counsel a pregnant fifteen-year-old who wishes to have an abortion? Can she count on him to look at her individual problem objectively and give her sound advice? I think it is safe to say that regardless of the circumstances surrounding the pregnancy or the girl's state of mind, the answer will surely be negative in regard to having an abortion.

Some time ago I was employed on the pediatric service of a Midwestern Catholic hospital. I was called by a nurse to start an intravenous infusion on a three-year-old girl who was suffering from pneumonia. Upon arriving at the girl's bedside, I was struck by her multiple birth defects: her hands had no fingers, her face was grotesque, and she was profoundly mentally retarded. I became interested in the girl's history, which was given to me by the attending nurse.

The girl was the product of a father-daughter consanguineous relationship within a strict Catholic household. (The odds of a child having major birth defects as a result of an incestuous mating are hundreds of times greater than for any other child.) In compliance with Church teachings, an abortion was never considered. This child was born although her birth defects were very predictable.

At the very best, this child can look forward to a short life in an institution. And the mother of this child will go through life with the knowledge that she gave birth to her own father's child. The psychological implications of this are devastating.

Most Catholic priests have all but been programmed to feel as they do and so are often incapable of looking objectively at a problem with two sides or multiple solutions. If the same fifteen-year-old girl mentioned before returned to the same priest a year later to request permission to prevent another pregnancy via contraception, she might again get a negative answer or the ludicrous advice to abstain from sexual intercourse.

Many clergymen tell their congregations, "Thou shalt not do what I don't like to do"; and I question the motivation of some Catholic priests who maintain such a hard line on contraception and abortion. Could it be that they harbor a conscious or unconscious resentment because they are shut off from something in which they would like to have a part?

The Psychotherapist as a Clergyman

As I have pointed out, many highly trained psychiatrists are in effect clergymen in psychiatrists' clothing, for when a psychiatrist is guided by his religious beliefs in dealing with his patient, he is not really providing psychotherapy; he is reading an impromptu sermon. I contend that this is especially unfair to the patient whose religion is different from his psychiatrist's.

Neofanaticism on the Hippie Scene

Though hippies have become stereotyped as long-haired drug-users, they are represented by more than one kind of person and constitute a good-sized minority segment of our population. They exist on different levels, some being hard-core narcotics abusers who support their expensive habits with various modes of crime. Somewhere in the middle of the continuum is the flower child (many think he is a dying breed), who seems to have sincere beliefs about peace and other good causes and who generally gravitates toward the political left. At the other end of the spectrum there exists probably the largest group of "hippies," usually products of middle- and upper-middle-class homes. With the aid of Madison Avenue they emulate the other two hippie groups.

The three groups have relatively little in common other than mode of dress, hairstyles, musical taste, other super-ficialities, and certainly drug usage, which varies from narcotics, amphetamines, and psychedelics to marijuana. Parents ponder sullenly about their children going off to school in "rags," not realizing the motivation for this. Among other reasons, it seems to be an impotent attempt by the adolescent to imitate the process of growing up the "hard way" (something most of them have been deprived of) as perhaps his parents had to. Salvation Army stores are having a heyday selling tattered clothing to these kids. The torn pair of jeans becomes a symbol of hard knocks and allows the adolescent to experience the vicarious pleasure of seeming to "make it on his own."

Another characteristic of this group is their tendency to

gravitate toward various aspects of the occult—for example, astrology. The pseudoscience of astrology, a dying art only a few years ago, has been reincarnated by these people (again aided by Madison Avenue) and has become big business. Astrological symbols have acquired renewed meanings and suddenly with the help of a musical bonanza we are made aware of the Aquarian Age.

More recent than the astrological craze in this subculture is a new brand of religious prostitution, the Jesus craze. Large numbers of young people are now jumping on this bandwagon, supported by a rock opera. The claim seems to be that they have found a whole new meaning in Christ, are closer to him, and understand him better than did past generations. Obviously, many of these people emulate Christ by grooming and dressing as He did; one gets the feeling now, more than ever before, that Christ is indeed ubiquitous—He can be found on any college campus, at rock festivals, or at other gatherings of the young.

Many of the "Jesus Freaks" claim to have substituted Christ for drugs; others prefer their indulgence with Christ in a drug milieu; many insist that a vision initiated this renaissance. Superficially, these movements have tremendous potential for good, especially if they offer an alternative to drug abuse. Often, however, the use of religion by these people is characterized by overzealousness for the same reasons that drugs have been so popular. A dissociative experience occurs with drugs as well as with this brand of religion. It provides for a means of incomplete escape from reality and is potentially a threat to the person's mental well-being. Very simply, a dissociative experience is a feeling of unrelatedness to the surrounding environment; even a feeling of detachment from oneself.

Countless adolescents seek in drug use this partial escape

from reality because, for various reasons, they perceive their reality as unpleasant. If the adolescent eventually shows subtle or profound signs of mental decompensation (for example, a psychotic reaction), it becomes difficult not to implicate the drugs at least as a contributory factor in the illness.

Sudden profound religious indulgence may provide an adolescent with a similar escape from reality-based conflicts; the procrastination of facing the conflict, combined with the dissociation of a profound religious experience, can rival drugs in their harmful effects. In other words, religion can be misused as an escape from reality and provide a refuge from dealing with conflicts. Such an escape challenges, in a way similar to LSD and other drugs, one's ability to maintain mental stability.

Some of these youth groups require an intensive initiation period for membership. This time is devoted to a concentrated dogmatic indoctrination. Emphasis is on literal Biblical interpretation and strong commitment to converting others, and the leaders of these movements are respected as authority figures by their disciples (a repetition of Biblical history).

Many who join these cults are past or present drug-users who often find the combination of Christ and hallucinogens a palatable cocktail, leading to an unreal trip. (I am not presenting such case histories because they may seem to repeat previous ones.) I foresee continued expansion of this movement and an increase in related problems.

7

Religion: Its Uses and Potentials

Some people claim that religion with its implicit belief in God is necessary for healthy mental adaptation. The presumptuous proponents of this hypothesis are really saying something very different: they are, in effect, redefining mental health by saying that it must include a foundation of religious beliefs.

This theorizing seems to overlook the fact that there are millions of mentally well-adjusted people who are, for the most part, nonreligious. I am nevertheless convinced that religion, while potentially a negative influence, is very often a supportive and even enriching force that can facilitate mental well-being and general happiness.

It is the manner by which one is introduced to (and the way one practices) religion that determines the kind of influence it will ultimately exercise. All but the most naïve people realize that no religion is without its merits and faults; but every person indulges his religion in a different way and to a varying degree. With all these variables operating, it is apparent that it is the individual himself, not the religious hierarchy, that allows religious beliefs to influence his life to a greater or lesser degree and in a "good" or "bad" manner.

92

It is impossible to quantify a person's degree of religiosity, just as happiness and anxiety cannot be measured. As the previous chapters point out, though, overindulgence is potentially hazardous; the patients I discussed were quite religious, at least during some period of their life. On the other hand, many hyperreligious people are living happily and functioning effectively with the aid of (or in spite of) relative overzealousness. This happens because of the inherent and infinitely variable capacity of people to deal with life more or less effectively. It can also be explained by the varying quality of their religious practices.

At one end of a spectrum I see people thoughtfully participating in what I arbitrarily call a "good" brand of religion. At the other extreme are those who blindly plunge into a potentially "harmful" brand of religion. Just as only a minority of heavy smokers develop lung cancer, only a minority of blindly plunging worshipers will suffer problems.

While any particular religious denomination can be good or harmful for participants, some religious sects are good for people more often than others. It would be presumptuous of me (although I am tempted) to attempt drafting a consumer's checklist rating various religions in a manner similar to the way a consumer magazine rates dishwashers. I cannot, on the other hand, ignore the fact that some religious sectors thrive on their attraction for the naïve and mentally ill and actually contribute to mental illness.

From my experience, I tend to look with a jaundiced eye at the more fundamental and/or evangelical Protestant faiths, and I directly question the conscious motives of many of their clergymen. They seem to preach the most hazardous brand of religion, and for this reason I would start any checklist by rating these religious movements at the bottom.

With very few exceptions, most religions become harmful only when taken incorrectly or in overdosage. There probably are strengths inherent in every religion practiced in this country today, and one of these strengths is inculcation of the concept of a God.

The Concept of God

One of the most basic of religious beliefs is that there exists, in some form or place, something called God. It is safe to say that most, if not all, religions have something to say about God. Many people, for a variety of reasons, have at some time questioned their belief in God and attempted to deny the existence of a God, but the denial is often only transient. Most people seem to feel more comfortable believing in God; it is this very comfort that encourages the belief and maintains it.

I think that because such a belief serves to help sustain mental stability for most people, individuals deny belief in God only with reluctance. Even many atheists are quick to admit regret over their inability to initiate and maintain this very desirable belief.

A very common contemporary malady is what I would call existentialist depression. Anyone can experience this to some degree, but it is most common among college students, college professors, and intellectually oriented people in general. The symptoms of this depression are not unlike those of other depressive reactions, but the cause seems to be different.

The empty feeling associated with this malady is an offshoot of a style of thinking that seems to have reached a pinnacle today. Very simply, this philosophy, shared by many people, portrays a randomly organized purposeless universe in which man resides accidentally. He therefore lives without purpose and is doomed to an existence which is antagonistic to nature. Man ultimately dies and nature goes on without him as if he had never existed.

As to purpose, this philosophy places man on par with insects; that is to say, he has no real meaning in life and serves only to procreate and eventually to die. This philosophy is unfortunately supported by much sound scientific observation and prediction. For example, calculations by Isaac Asimov preclude the egocentric contention that earth has a monopoly on life. The theories and observations of Albert Einstein drive home the facts that the earth, relatively speaking, is a speck of dust and the sun (a somewhat larger speck of dust) will sustain any form of life on our planet for only a finite period.

I have personally found that as one reads such material, one may feel reduced first to the size of a Lilliputian and later to infinite smallness. Such feelings of uselessness and smallness can lead to a generally depressive outlook. This pattern of thinking is exceedingly common, self-perpetuating, and certainly can lead to despair and even suicide. (I would surmise that it might sometimes explain mysterious and apparently motiveless suicides, especially among people of high academic stature and apparent success.) Though intellectuals most typically find themselves in this philosophical rut, they are not without company. Most people who are at all introspective have wrestled with this problem to some degree.

A belief in God helps to prevent this vicious cyclic thought pattern and/or tends to neutralize it because belief in a personal God is the antithesis of this philosophy. It is certainly egocentric of man to believe that there is a God who listens to *him*, responds to *him*, helps *him*, and inflicts tragedy on *him*.

Believing in God allows man to be egocentric and, in

doing so, allows man to become important, at least to himself. Believing in God tends to preclude the concept of a purposeless universe and meaningless existence. The person who is able to obtain and sustain such a faith is not plagued by the ominous feeling that he is only a pawn of nature.

My personal observations of atheists support these contentions. What happens to people who do not believe in God? A disproportionate number of the atheists I have known seem to be preoccupied with the thought that they are merely specks of dust, parasites on a larger speck of dust, and so on. They are able to arrive at their conclusions through tenacious logic, which is intellectually fulfilling but spiritually empty. It is, I think, this spiritual vacuum that leads to the hopeless feelings of depression. If all belief in God were suddenly to cease, the incidence of depression would surely skyrocket. Consequently, I look at a belief in God technically as a defense against depression and I regard this "defense" as an exceedingly healthy one.

A personal concept of or belief in God, whether He be a creator, manipulator, or whatever, is not a necessity for mental health and happiness; it is, rather, a facilitator that creates a meaning for living (a meaning that might otherwise not exist for some people). Herein lies one of religion's greatest treasures: belief in God is an offering that in itself not only justifies religion, but often compensates for its frequent shortcomings.

Throughout time man seems to have found a general need for a God from whom he could derive meaning for his life. In some countries where atheism seems to be a national policy there is an attempt to substitute nationalism for God. The people of the Soviet Union are encouraged to "live for the state." I question this all too concrete God-substitute and doubt that it remains effective for very long.

In some cases God or related figures, such as Christ, may serve another valuable need. Referring again to psychoanalytic theory, it is almost universally accepted that the developing child models himself after his parents via the mechanism of identification. The child identifies with his parents and in many ways behaves like them, even to the most subtle mannerisms. He also tends to adopt the parents' system of morals and other essential concepts.

Unfortunately, numerous children have only one parent, no parents, or bad parents. In any of these situations a child is handicapped. If his father is a gangster, he may identify with the father and become a gangster himself. But the child who lacks a positive source of identification may turn to his church to seek an alternative object of identification. He may look at Christ not just as a Biblical figure, but as an object with which to identify. This alternate figure of authority may have a profound positive effect upon a child. The local clergyman himself may become a very gratifying object of identification, and is then in a position to do an inordinate amount of good with such a child.

In a more general sense, the child may use the church as a basic guideline from which to learn and grow. This may be a more desirable alternative to what is waiting for him at home. In this spirit the child may learn to know right from wrong and learn to love within a family even if his parents have failed to master any of these basics.

Consequently, a personal concept of God can inject meaning into life where previously there was lack of direction; it can provide a positive figure of authority where there is otherwise a negative authority or no authority.

I would like to emphasize my views with the use of a syllogism: All religions tend to incorporate a belief in some kind of God; belief in a God *can* facilitate happiness and mental stability; all religion *can* be potentially gratifying to the person who practices it.

Religion's Role in the Acceptance of Mortality

Few people live who have not fantasized the grandeur of immortality. Just as man always seeks to find meaning in life, he anticipates meaning in death, even though, of course, he dreads it. Existentialists and atheists look upon death as the end of the road, a road that therefore leads nowhere. This, in turn, logically leads back to the feeling that the life that precedes death is a futility.

I have seen a fair number of people with terminal illnesses and have observed how they face impending death. While few are happy at the thought of death, the person without religion often is the most angry and uncomfortable with this burden. Many religious persons, especially those believing in an afterlife, are more accepting and tolerant in their final days. They approach death not as the end, but as transition.

For many good reasons it is becoming the vogue for doctors to be more frank with patients regarding serious or terminal illness. It is important for the family as well as the patient to be informed of the implications of a predictable fatality. If the entire family (including the patient) knows the situation, open communication is possible between the dying person and his family. If the patient's prognosis is kept a secret from him, the family will tend to be covert, insincere, and set apart from him. He becomes isolated from the family at the very time when he needs their support the most.

Physicians and nurses are therefore being trained to treat the dying patient with openness as well as empathy. This is not without its problems: the person who is made aware of his terminal condition must somehow deal with this burden. Obviously, a patient's reaction often is depression and extreme withdrawal. Belief in an afterlife, as encouraged by most religious faiths, helps the dying person to accept his fate. Just as religion can provide a philosophic purpose in life through God, it provides a "purpose" in death through the concept of afterlife.

Whether or not an afterlife exists is of little importance to the dying person who is able to fantasize that it does exist. For even if it turns out that the afterlife is a myth, the fantasying of it can serve a purpose right up to the last heart contraction. Atheists and existentalists often enjoy debating or "proving" the nonexistence of the hereafter, which in my opinion is often a defensive maneuver. I feel that such attempts to dispel these beliefs represent a resentment by these people that they are not able to believe in the very concept they seemingly deplore.

It is a sour-grapes rationalization: "Since I am unable to believe in heaven, I will prove to the world that heaven does not logically exist."

I surmise that the concept of God and the hereafter are two of the most useful beliefs any religion has to offer. Many religions, in fact, would be better off if they offered only these concepts as their total repertoire.

Often, when these ideas are embellished, the overall concepts become more difficult to grasp. More people would accept the existence of an afterlife if they were given a less fully illustrated picture of it. If religions allowed for more fantasy or use of one's imagination, more people would digest the thought of a heaven. It is almost as though "one can't see the forest" for the pearly gates.

Fortunately, it seems that more and more clergymen are

becoming less and less naïve about what people can and cannot accept and thus are better able to talk about heaven without giving one a guided tour. Greek mythology, though fascinating, is not taken seriously any more because it was too descriptive and concrete. It is difficult to believe in a God who has a name, image, and personality. I would urge clergymen to allow their congregations to develop religious concepts in a less structured but more digestible fashion. People are becoming increasingly sophisticated, and some of today's Occidental religions may become tomorrow's Greek mythology.

We are living at a time when lay people are urging their religious organizations to take on more diversification and provide for more authority and guidance. I think it is healthier for people to delineate their own stance on issues, and to do so on their own authority. I would hope that religious organizations could concentrate more in their area of expertise—a concept of God and an afterlife—for it is here that people in general will benefit most from their religious experience, especially in times of tragedy, such as imminent death.

Just as the dying person can be comforted by religious ideas, so can the bereaved family. The death of a loved one leaves in its wake a residue of difficult-to-deal-with feelings. Primarily, these are feelings of depression or grief, guilt, and hopelessness; these feelings are part of a single complex and must be dealt with by any person in mourning.

At the outset of mourning many people are unsure of how they should react: they want to assume the "proper" attitude toward the lost loved one. It is at this initial point that a person may derive needed support from his religious faith, beginning with the funeral ritual. The funeral provides a socially acceptable and tangible occasion to mourn in public. The group assembled at this gathering provides strength for the mourners and reinforcement of the realization that the loved one is indeed gone. Before the mourning period can really begin, a person must come to accept this reality; this may sometimes be difficult because some people tend unconsciously to deny that the death actually occurred.

When funerals turn into festive and joyous gatherings with an aura of cheerfulness they supposedly cheer up the bereaved. I am certain that this happens, at least temporarily. On the surface this may appear to be a healthy exercise, but usually it serves only to delay mourning. The person who has just lost a loved one is not in need of cheering up; he needs empathy and sympathy. He will invariably interpret cheering-up attempts as superficial platitudes, which indeed they are.

Because the theme of most religious funerals is one of sympathy and solemnity, not cheerfulness, the event usually serves to support the bereaved through the empathy of others. Some funeral celebrations stress profound sorrowful emotional release, with encouragement of a good deal of weeping. This may call to mind my earlier references to the unreality of Pentecostal meetings and the potential hazards that this entails. But in mourning this does not apply. The emotional weeping is appropriate and related to a very real happening—death.

Though I am not personally of this cultural-religious persuasion, I tend to think of it as a most healthy kind of funeral ritual. Venting of emotions, if genuine, must certainly accelerate the mourning process by alleviating or releasing some of the emotional burden we all experience at such a time.

In addition to the funeral itself, other religious concepts come into play, aiding the bereaved and the dying—if they have faith. If a person really believes that a heaven exists, he can look at the loss of a loved one not as a "death," but as a temporary separation to be followed by a reunion at the time of his own death.

I recall a seventy-eight-year-old patient dying from the complications of chronic leukemia. His wife had died fourteen years earlier and the man had subsequently lived by himself in loneliness. I was on duty as an intern and was called by the nurse to pronounce him dead. She told me that several days before the imminent finality he expressed to her the desire for death so that he could rejoin his wife. He lived out his last days in anticipation of seeing his wife again—an anticipation made possible by the man's faith in the existence of an afterlife.

It is difficult to determine why some people accept the concept of an afterlife and others reject it, but I reiterate that the most avid skeptics are avid out of regret.

The bereaved may find solace in belief for another reason: if he believes that the universe is a purposeful, structured creation of God, he can infer that there was purpose in the life that just ended. It would logically follow that there is purpose in death and other tragedy as well. Out of this mode of thinking comes the cliché often uttered in times of tragedy, "It was God's will."

For a person to think that God has specifically willed a tragedy to his family is egocentric thinking in its highest form. The person who "miraculously" lives through an auto accident, in which the car died, is equally egocentric to think that God specifically saved him from impending doom. Despite the egocentricity, however, such thoughts can give comfort and reassurance to the person who has faith. I do not mention this as a plea for religions to become completely based upon logic. All one's beliefs need not be founded on logic and proof. This is where the cybernetic analogy with man falls apart: his mind and emotions cannot be compared with the workings of a computer.

Religion: A Portable Cultural Milieu

Our society lives in a perpetual state of migration. For some people frequent moving from city to city is a necessity dictated by employment or educational opportunities. For the latter reason I have personally made six major moves in the past ten years. For many, moving is uncomfortable and cumbersome; the discomfort usually does not subside for several months. While the miserable mechanics of moving are a transient problem, the acclimatization to a new community can be an extremely unpleasant and drawn-out experience. This is especially true if the move is not one of choice—for example, being transferred from an Army base in San Francisco to one in Rose Bud, South Dakota.

Even when a particular move is greatly desired by a person, he may commonly experience a period of depression associated with the various losses incurred by moving away from the point of departure. Perhaps the greatest single loss is a feeling of security founded on the person's familiarity with his former home. Moving to a new city may mean the loss of friends, a familiar home, a desirable climate, or even a favorite restaurant. Establishing some kind of roots in a new locale is an absolute necessity for most people; without this, the very desirable feeling of security may not be achieved. It is here that a church may play a vital role.

One advantage of organized religion is that it provides for the establishment of relatively standardized religious subcommunities across the country. For the newcomer this provides some instant familiarity within the community, complete with a place to go and arrangements to meet people with whom he has at least something in common.

Americans demand this kind of ubiquitous standardization, a fact clearly demonstrated by the success of many retail chain stores. Absurd as it may seem, millions of people enjoy traveling all over the country, only to stay in hotels and motels as identical as those on a Monopoly board. They eat identical tasteless hamburgers served at equally identical drive-in restaurants. I think this reflects a general need or desire to "feel at home" when not at home.

I know of a career Army family that takes moving in stride with the aid of organized religion. Upon arrival at a new base (an event occurring almost every other year), their first activity is to seek out and affiliate with one of the local Lutheran churches. They use the church as a nucleus around which to build up an involvement with the new community. They view the base officers' club as their only alternative to a church nucleus for meeting people socially and developing relationships. The church offers them an opportunity for total family involvement in the new community and renders them much less dependent upon base activities. Because dependence on the officers' club often fosters a parallel alcoholic dependence, the choice of church becomes not only a convenient alternative, but a more healthy and effective mode of adaptation: It consistently works well for many people and is available for countless others who avoid it.

The affiliation with a church, then, provides a portable cultural milieu that a person or family can transport from one city to another when moving or even while traveling (few houses of worship discourage visiting guests). Only certain people can take advantage of this opportunity, for if one is to "feel at home" in a new-community church, he must have a genuine sense of religious identity. Without such an identity, a new church will be as foreign as the city in which it is located.

The college student away from home for the first time may find some comfort from participation in campus religious activities, but only if he has had a previous emotional investment in a particular organized religion. Without some prior commitment, the desirable feeling of security and comfort is sure to be lessened.

It is currently a fad of the younger generation to scoff at organized or institutionalized religion. In denigrating these established institutions, they criticize the money wasted on building elaborate churches and synagogues; they insist that group prayer is phony, and resent hackneyed dogmatisms. While there is some merit in these criticisms, there exists a blindness for the possible advantages of organization and standardization. The sense of group religious identity and the "portable cultural milieu" are very desirable offshoots, made possible only by the fact that religion has been so highly organized. This, in my opinion, is a very real justification for religious systems.

The Concepts of Prayer versus Worry

Prayer is an interesting and ancient phenomenon that holds widely varying meanings for different people. On the most fundamental level are those people who believe in a personal God; for them God listens to (and responds with respect to) prayer much in the same manner that a parent listens and responds to his child. This conception of a living, hearing God is not surprising in light of the fact that man has made or perceived God in his own image—for example, "May God let his countenance shine upon you and give you peace."

Most clergymen seem to foster this concept of God and also encourage their congregations to pray. Countless other people are not certain that God listens, but derive comfort from prayer anyway. Again like children speaking to parents, people request all kinds of things and attempt to fend off other things through prayer. To name a few: "Show me the way"; "Allow me to live longer"; "Please don't punish me"; "Help me to lose weight."

At least for the moment I choose to sidestep the issue of whether or not God listens to prayer because, to be completely frank, no one can know, and I certainly do not know either. I am sure, though, that it would be extremely boring for God to listen to all that responsive reading week after week and just think of all those television stations that sign off every night with the Lord's Prayer! If God does listen to prayer, so much the better.

But there exist other, more tangible effects of praying about which I do know something.

As all students of Freudian psychology are aware, the undesirable feeling of anxiety is often controlled by a variety of processes known as defense mechanisms (repression has already been mentioned). Some of these mechanisms tend to be healthy and anxiety-reducing, while the excessive use of less healthy ones will lead to neurosis and psychosis.

I look at prayer as another mechanism that is efficacious in controlling anxiety, but it is a healthy mechanism. It appears to be closely associated with the process of worry, which is sometimes healthy, but often not as effective or healthy as prayer, its analogue. The control of anxiety is a primary accomplishment of prayer that can be easily demonstrated.

On numerous occasions a person in distress might freely interchange prayer and worry. Take, for example, Wilbur, who has a flight phobia and is about to embark on his first trip to Europe via airliner. As the plane taxis down the runway of a New York airport, he begins to perspire profusely and senses a significant increase in his pulse rate. As the plane ascends Wilbur feels an emptiness in his chest and a tingling sensation all over. He is having not a heart attack, but rather an anxiety attack; he is worried that the wings are going to separate from the fuselage and that he will be severely injured. His worry has little basis in reality, but his subjective anxiety is only too real. Continued worry provides a parade of horrors based upon his memories of hijack headlines and war movies.

If Wilbur is a man of some faith, he may commence to pray that God provide some additional protection and reassurance. Again, it is egocentric of Wilbur to think that God will specifically protect his plane with more than the usual zeal, but egocentric or not, this man begins to feel strengthened as he prays and his anxiety is reduced.

Wilbur's mother, back in Poughkeepsie, is also praying for her son, which demonstrates yet another benefit of this religious ritual. She is aware that there is really nothing she can do to insure her son's safety. She is not on the plane and knows nothing of airplanes anyway, but through prayer she is able, at least vicariously, to help protect her son. Through the process of prayer she is assured that she has "done" everything possible for her son and feels better herself about the flight. Even if the plane should crash, which is exceedingly unlikely, she could reflect on how the disaster occurred only in spite of her attempts to prevent this through prayer.

Most people turn to genuine personal prayer only in

times of tragedy. Serious illness commonly provides a stimulus for worry and prayer; the dynamics of such a situation are much the same as those operating with Wilbur and his mother. The ultimate feeling of helplessness is realized by a person whose loved one is critically ill. As a physician I have often observed family members hovering at the bedside of a dying person; candid observation reveals feelings of grief and hopelessness, but especially helplessness. These people not only want to do something, but feel as though they *must* do something.

If, as is usually the case, these people have no practical knowledge of medicine or nursing, they are limited in what they can do to alter the situation. It is here that prayer may play a very positive role. The woman praying for her afflicted husband is accomplishing at least two things: she feels as though she is doing something and she alleviates some anxiety. If she merely worries about the situation, her level of anxiety will increase. Prayer offers her a vicarious but seemingly effective opportunity to be of some help; the positive ramifications are abundant and obvious.

So people are wise to turn to spontaneous personal prayer instead of worry. Worrying is a rumination process: uneasy thoughts are repetitively reviewed by the worrier. He becomes temporarily obsessed with his worrisome ideas. This inevitably leads to a magnification process that in turn produces additional worry. The result is a vicious cycle producing more and more anxiety.

The fact that worry leads to an intensification of anxiety is not always bad, a contention supported by the testimonials of people in the performing arts. The pianist who is about to play a concerto may worry about the possibility of making a mistake; the worrying is converted into increasing anxiety. Mediated through a complex series of instantaneous physiological and biochemical alterations, the anxiety makes for a better musical performance. In this case the harnessed anxiety, initiated and amplified by worry, serves a useful purpose for the virtuoso. With Wilbur, however, anxiety heightened with his plane's ascent and served no positive purpose; it merely led to feelings of discomfort.

Worry varies from useful to harmful, depending upon the situation. It may also vary with respect to the quantity of anxiety produced. If our virtuoso worried *excessively*, the resultant anxiety might have become overwhelming; and he might have become temporarily disabled as a pianist. At that point prayer might have been of considerable assistance.

Just as in previous consideration of the afterlife, prayer justifies itself by the subjective alleviation of anxiety that results from it. People derive direct benefit from prayer by readjusting their own anxiety to more tolerable levels. In addition, they are able to savor the vicarious pleasure of having done something either for themselves or someone else (Wilbur and his mother, respectively, for example), when in reality they are unable to do something more tangible. It is this vicarious feeling of pleasure or accomplishment that separates prayer from worry; worry can only intensify ruminations about consequences and anticipations, thereby increasing uneasiness.

In summary, prayer can be a healthy mechanism that "defends" its user from anxiety. A person with enough religious faith to believe in prayer has another effective personal weapon with which to approach life stresses.

Thus far I have been referring only to spontaneous and individual prayer. I suspect that organized prayer, as prescribed by institutionalized religion, is much less efficacious and much more ritualistic. Prayer in this form is so stereo-

typed and generalized that it misses the mark in the amelio-
ration of anxiety. If nothing else, though, it at least provides
a prototype for individual prayer; it may serve as a dress
rehearsal for a later time when a more genuine kind of
prayer may be urgently needed.

The theologian may insist that I have dehydrated the
entire issue of prayer, for he attempts to instill into his
congregation the concept that prayer is homage to God.
This is certainly a beautiful idea for those who are able to
accept such a personal (egocentric) conception of God. I
have merely added to this conception my feelings about
prayer as a vent for anxiety and substitute for worry
because this is a tangible benefit that is observed over and
over again.

Religion: Prophylaxis Against Suicide

Suicide represents the ultimate tragedy of mental illness
and accounts for tens of thousands of deaths every year in
this country. The histories behind given suicides vary
considerably. In the psychotic, especially the schizophrenic,
misinterpretation of reality can provide the motivation for
killing oneself. Such a person may, for example, accidentally commit suicide in an attempt to rid himself of his "bad
part." He reasons that when the bad part is dead, he will be
left with the remaining "good part." This kind of delusional
thinking pattern has often accounted for a suicide attempt.

In nonpsychotic people depression, not delusion,
accounts for thoughts or acts of suicide, usually, if not
always. Certainly the most common general complaint of
psychiatric patients is depression and for many of these
patients suicide becomes a desirable, if reluctantly taken,
step.

A suicide attempt may represent a means of calling for help, punishing a loved one through a symbolic murder, or, less often, a genuine attempt to terminate an unhappy life. Regardless of what desire lies behind a suicide, any given attempt can result in death by intent or accident.

I have worked with many patients who expressed the desire to commit suicide but were sidetracked from acting on this desire because of strong, forbidding religious beliefs. Though I cannot directly assess how frequent this is, a disproportionate number of these people have been devout Catholics. I sincerely believe, as others do, that many suicides are prevented directly by this religious taboo. This allows an unhappy person to seek a reversible alternative to his depression.

While this kind of very direct religious prophylaxis can be demonstrated through numerous case histories, a more indirect and intangible preventive element also exists. I refer again to the positive effect of religion in warding off the negative feelings associated with existentialist depression. Religion, by injecting some meaning and order into life (where otherwise there may be none), provides a "reason" or purpose for continuing life and therefore for resisting suicide.

Religion: A Therapeutic Adjunct?

Mental health has long been a frustrating national problem: we have all been bombarded with statistics; for example, 10 per cent of the nation's population is at some time in life hospitalized with a psychiatric problem. Added to the general shortage of mental health personnel, this makes for sloppy efforts to catch up with the problem.

This pressing need has resulted in the prostitution of the

encounter group concept. This form of therapy—valid when supervised by competent leaders—is being carried out on a large scale by people whose professional experience varies from impressive to nonexistent. The goal seems to be to put an encounter group in every large business, church, and garage. Among the lay people who have been organizing and/or supervising such groups are many clergymen. The house of worship is getting into the act and becoming a part-time community mental health center. It has become the scene not only of encounter groups, but of counseling services as well.

This provides an opportunity for churches and synagogues to do inordinate amounts of good or harm. Though I am somewhat skeptical about religion's direct participation, sensible, competently trained clergymen can offer their services and really help people with significant emotional problems. I feel very strongly, though, that any clergyman who assumes the role and responsibility of a "therapist" should receive direct professional supervision.

A minister, priest, or rabbi should consult a qualified mental health professional on a regular basis in order to discuss the ramifications of his "patients'" conflicts. Without such guidance, even the most well-meaning and intelligent clergyman may have difficulty in diagnosing or treating emotional problems. What may on the surface appear to be a neurotic depression to a rabbi may look more like a brain tumor to a psychiatrist.

With regard to the popular encounter group bandwagon, I think clergymen should stay away. It takes a considerable amount of skill and experience to lead such a group thoughtfully. The clergyman, armed only with a book on group psychotherapy, is a veritable bull in a china shop and the results can be a good deal worse. People are more valuable than glassware.

I have seen instances in which a qualified clinical psychologist acts as a cotherapist with a clergyman in running church-centered therapy sessions. This can become an enriching experience for everyone involved and should be encouraged. This is one way for the church to reach people who are, for various reasons, beyond the reach of assistance from mental health professionals.

8

How to Teach Your Children
a Healthy Attitude about Religion:
a Parents' Guide

Religion is not unlike sex: those with a healthy attitude toward it can derive a great deal of satisfaction from it while others only become frustrated with it.

I once read in a newspaper question-answer column a question submitted by a child who complained that his mother was forcing religious beliefs upon him, insisting that he attend church, study the Bible, and participate in related activity. The columnist advised the child that his parent was acting correctly and that he should feel grateful. The writer went on to quote the commandment "Honor thy father and thy mother" and instructed the child that God was referring to this child's kind of mother.

I interpreted the answer as, "Do what you're told, you ungrateful kid!" The article closed by encouraging the child to listen to his mother's advice in order to be spared heartache later.

I was aghast when I read this and immediately sympathized with the unfortunate child.

This parent was acting not out of faith or love, but out of arbitrariness. For a child to become motivated enough to write such a letter, he must be sensing a significant conflict about his religious attitude vis-à-vis his parents' beliefs. The fact that the child perceived a conflict indicated that he was attempting to think and act with an air of independence; this is unequivocally a healthy trend in any child. His rigid parent, on the other hand, was not about to stand for such dissension, but was, rather, bent upon stuffing religion down the child's gullet.

The columnist, via his authoritarian answer, unilaterally supported the misguided parent and concomitantly stifled the child with a punishment in the form of an injunction from the Ten Commandments. By citing this awesome source and using it as he did, the implicit message was an equation of respect for religion and parent. The implicit message, then, was "Because you do not honor your parent's religion, you do not honor your parent!"

This implies an eleventh commandment: "Thou shalt love and honor thy religion and not question it." It acts to inculcate the "fail-safe," something that may eventually smother this child's independent thinking processes. (The reader will recall, from Chapter 2, that the "fail-safe" is a religious mechanism with which a person "protects" himself from seeing a point of view differing from his own. The implicit "Thou shalt not question thy religion" protects a person from alien ideas that might challenge his chosen beliefs and is an illustration of my "fail-safe" principle.)

Worst of all, the inquiring child is certain to feel guilty on reading the columnist's answer. What kind of rotten kid refuses to honor his parents? Furthermore, if this parent continues to force religious beliefs on the child, the latter may tend not only to resist the beliefs, but to rebel against the mother in general. The outcome will certainly be one of two probable scenarios:

The child's independence and resistance will begin to break down and he will tend to assimilate the mother's beliefs. With regard to religion, the child will grow up making liberal usage of the "filter effect" and "fail-safe" and will become arbitrary in his spiritual thinking. The child will tend to inflict religion similarly upon *his* children ("Do unto others as they have done unto you").

Or the child will continue to resist his mother and her efforts and will begin to develop a more personal and flexible mode of religious thinking. His relationship with his mother may become relatively distant and he may eventually give up religion completely or convert to another.

I begin with this tragic example not because it is so negative but so typical. It demonstrates the parental attitude that is frequently responsible for alienating many children from religion. Before discussing alternative approaches to this and other conflicts, some general comments are in order.

In teaching of religious attitudes throughout the various stages of childhood, the parent must be aware of certain characteristics inherent in each of these stages if he hopes to do a thoughtful job. The dividing lines between the three stages vary with each child, but they can be approximated arbitrarily by age. Stages 1 and 2 can be separated into preschool (ages 0 to six) and school-age children (ages six to twelve). Stage 3 begins at age thirteen and continues as long as the child lives at home with his parents.

Stage 1 (ages 0 to six)

The Stage 1 child has relatively immature thought processes and thinks on a very different plane from older children. He thinks, so to speak, in a vertical directon; he is able to perceive and learn, but only on a very concrete level. This child's thought processes can be equated with the trunk of a tree. He is able to learn about whatever he sees, but is less able to integrate abstract material. He can identify and later recognize, for example, a ball or a dog, but he cannot fathom such intangible concepts as "energy," "gravity," or "tranquillity." Even though the word "energy" may be in his vocabulary, he is not able to picture the actual concept.

Similarly, the preschool child, according to child psychiatrists and psychologists, is unable to appreciate the real meaning of death. He may recollect that Uncle George died last week, but he is unable really to appreciate George's fate and therefore may not appear to be particularly upset about it. It logically follows that the Stage 1 child is unable to grasp such concepts as God, heaven, hell, and a multitude of other related abstract religious concepts.

Stage 2 (ages six to twelve)

The Stage 2 child gradually acquires the ability to think on an additional plane that I call horizontal. His mind can function in more than one direction and now can be compared to the tree trunk with branches and leaves added. (What I am calling Stage 1 and 2 thinking, incidentally, is a simplistic paraphrasing of Freud's concept of primary-

and secondary-process thinking.) The Stage 2 child gradually achieves a mastery of abstract thinking and is able to
integrate less tangible ideas. He is able to grasp a meaning
and understanding of the concepts of death, energy, and
even God. If Uncle George dies when his nephew is ten,
the boy may grieve with the rest of the family, for he now
realizes George's fate.

Stage 3 (ages thirteen and over)

With the onset of Stage 3 comes a difficult period for the
child and his parents. It is during this period that he begins
to differentiate from others and turns into an independently
thinking individual, at least ideally. For some children this
will occur relatively early in the stage; for at least a few
others, it never occurs at all.

The transition from one of these stages to another is, of
course, gradual; precocious children may advance more
rapidly; emotionally ill children may advance slowly or
become fixated. Most children, though, seem to fit very
approximately into these stages. The characteristics that I
mention to define the stages are generally accepted by professionals in the field of personality development. I have
chosen particular characteristics that I feel are paramount
in teaching religion to children. This is not meant to be a
laconic outline of childhood personality development, but
rather a set of guidelines for an interested parent.

I believe that two factors are of special importance if the
teaching of religion is to result in a healthy attitude toward
it. The first is *the manner* in which religious material is
taught; the second is *the age* at which specific material is
presented.

Stage 1 Learning

I am quite concerned about the kind of Biblical material offered to a Stage 1 child in many Sunday Schools. He is unable to grasp the abstract meaning of God and heaven but is nevertheless exposed to these concepts. Because he cannot realize an abstract meaning for God, he must substitute a very naïve concrete meaning. He is taught about something that he cannot possibly hope to understand.

His interpretation of the most elementary Biblical presentation is therefore highly unpredictable. He is almost in the position of an English literature major who accidentally stumbles into a lecture on the physics of planetary motion. No matter how proficient and benign the Sunday School teacher might be, he cannot be certain that his class of five-year-olds understands much of the instruction.

At first glance it seems completely innocent to see children labor over Biblical coloring books, sing religious hymns, and parrot back Biblical tales. A closer look, however, reveals that much of this is far beyond a child's ability to understand. What occurs, then, is a very undesirable phenomenon: learning that precedes understanding.

The child "learns" a variety of stories about God, Jesus, and so on; the material is reinforced repeatedly and mastered on a very concrete level. But it is not understood; it is memorized. Not until years later does the child begin to conceptualize what he has "learned" so well. Similarly, a child of six could learn to reproduce Einstein's famous equation, $E=mc^2$, but why go to so much trouble? Many years must pass before the child can grasp the meaning of the formula.

This may all seem somewhat academic, but I believe

there are dangers lurking in this seemingly routine "cramming." The preschooler's immature mind is prematurely programmed with a barrage of religious intangibles. His memory of the material is rote; his confusion is plentiful, as his questions frequently show.

Example 1: Johnnie (age five)

JOHNNIE: Mommy, where does God live?

MOMMY: God lives in heaven, Johnnie, with all of the angels.

JOHNNIE: What's an angel, Mommy?

MOMMY: Oh, don't worry about that now, Johnnie. Christmas is a long way off. We'll talk about angels when Christmas comes.

JOHNNIE: Mommy, does God sleep in a bed like people do?

MOMMY: Uh, oh (*gasp*) no, Johnnie, He, ah, doesn't sleep. He just stays up in heaven.

JOHNNIE: But doesn't He get tired being up there all day without sleeping?

MOMMY: Let's talk about this some other time, Johnnie. You should be outside playing on a day like this.

The preceding, very typical, colloquy was grossly mishandled by the mother. Anybody would be hard put to find a good answer to Johnnie's original question, however, because the question has arisen from Johnnie's inability to deal with the abstract concept of a God which was presented to him at Sunday School.

Johnnie's mother quite incidentally—one might say unwittingly—has answered the question. But in doing so, she utilized an equally abstract concept: heaven. As a result, Johnnie's confusion was compounded. His next question might just as well have been "What is heaven?"

Interestingly, in the midst of this dialogue, Johnnie and his mother are asking impossible tasks of each other. She wants him to attend Sunday School and learn in a real sense of that word; he wants her to interpret what is impossible to learn. The cycle is vicious and the result is increasing confusion for Johnnie and frustration for Mommy.

A somewhat more guided colloquy might proceed in a very different direction:

> JOHNNIE: Mommy, where does God live?
>
> MOMMY: God doesn't live in places the way people do, Johnnie. He just lives. I know that this is hard to understand, but as you get older I will help you to understand this.

In this example Johnnie's mother has avoided sidestepping the issue—she has just delayed dealing with it. She has also avoided using one abstract concept to explain another. Her procrastination was wise because it was done in the spirit of honesty. The insightful mother was admitting to herself and to her son that the time for this discussion was later. Her reassurance to Johnnie—that she would later help him to understand these concepts—was indeed thoughtful. She was unable to answer the question completely, but then Johnnie would have been unable to understand a complete answer.

The entire dilemma could have been avoided if Johnnie's formal religious exposure had begun at a more reasonable age.

I feel that all preschool religious education is to be deplored because these children just cannot comprehend it. If, however, the preschooler is enrolled in Sunday School and does make such inquiries, the second example should generally be followed. That is, avoid answering a question with the use of abstract concepts and avoid overly detailed answers. Always assure the child that as he gets older he will be better able to comprehend what he now questions.

A basic rule always to keep in mind is that a preschooler, regardless how bright, is likely to be puzzled and frustrated by abstract concepts, of religion as well as any other subjects. For the same reasons I would hesitate to advocate physics and chemistry as part of the curriculum for a modern nursery school.

In addition to the immediate confusion that results from premature religious indoctrination, it sets the stage for later problems in religious interpretation. Although most of the time we are unaware of how a Stage 1 child perceives religious abstraction, early religious training has caused him to store away in his mind numerous religious symbols and ideas that he is unable to deal with or correlate with one another. And the ensuing misconceptions may even lead to uneasiness and fear.

I recall a five-year-old Jewish boy who was learning about Passover in Sunday School. He was exposed to the Old Testament story about the lamb that was sacrificed on Passover; the lamb's blood was smeared on the door lintels of Jewish homes so that the Angel of Death would pass over and spare their first-born sons while taking the Egyptians'. Unbeknownst to the Sunday School teacher, the story terrified the boy. Aware that Passover was approaching, he developed a very real feeling of fear that someone was going to "sacrifice" his dog and smear the blood on his parents' home—not a far-fetched notion for a five-year-old.

Eastertime fills the Sunday School classroom with equally terrifying and violent tales of Christ being tormented and nailed onto the cross. I question the wisdom of exposing such gore to children who have not even begun school and may not even have witnessed a good lynching on television.

I can recall hearing, at the age of seven or so, a story told to my Hebrew school class about a martyred rabbi. All I can remember is that the man's tongue and legs were cut off in the middle of the town square. A related story was told about a woman whose skin was raked off for similar reasons.

I do not recall the reasons, just the gore. This horrified me at the time, as I am sure it did my classmates. The Bible is filled with violence from Genesis to the end and I would no more expose my young children to this than I would subject them to a bullfight or a public execution.

I even question the justification for teaching the Ten Commandments to Stage 1 children.

Is it necessary specifically to teach a child of five that he should not kill? I wonder how many children ever considered the thought of killing—prior to Sunday School stimulation. Similarly, how should a six-year-old interpret "Thou shalt not commit adultery"? And is it really necessary to "teach" children to honor and love their parents? Would it not be more reasonable and appropriate for children to learn this intuitively, as most children will anyway?

It is abundantly clear to me that Biblical material is as inappropriate as biochemistry to teach not only to the preschooler, but to the younger Stage 2 child as well.

Stage 2 Learning

As the child proceeds well into Stage 2 and his religious training continues, he finds that he is now able to perceive or imagine the concepts of God, heaven, and so on. If, however, he was exposed to these ideas in Stage 1, his mind is already filled with naïve remnants of religious indoctrination. I feel that this previously learned material handicaps his immediate perceptions: he is unable to grasp religious abstraction without the influence of the prematurely learned material from Stage 1. The previously learned material has prejudiced his present thinking and fostered the use of the filter effect. His approach to religious dogma cannot suddenly become objective now. As he is exposed to new Sunday School material, he will modify it, through the "filter effect," before he can assimilate it.

For example, Janet is an eight-year-old who is attempting to describe for herself a concept of heaven. (As pointed out earlier, if Janet is able to develop a genuine belief in heaven and the afterlife, she may be better off in the face of tragedy someday.) For her really to believe in this very abstract idea, she must accept it on her own terms: the belief has to be personal and genuine in order to be useful. If, because of her Stage 1 training, she already imagines heaven as a giant pearly edifice just beyond the moon, she will have some difficulty in Stage 2 in delineating a more sophisticated "heaven" in her mind. In order to take on a meaningful belief of heaven, she must first deal with her old beliefs, a side-effect of premature training.

Though I am not enthusiastic about Sunday School training for children younger than age seven or eight, I think much can be done to make the experience more benign for these younger children. Biblical tales should be kept to a minimum and on a superficial level; time might be better spent teaching general religious traditions and customs.

For example, at Hanukkah time I see little harm in teaching a five-year-old the traditional candle-lighting ceremony The bloody basis for the holiday could be saved for later.

Similarly, the Christmas customs of tree-decorating, family togetherness, and Christmas carols can be introduced to children early; however, the idea of the "Son of God" being born of a "virgin" could be postponed a few years until the child is well into Stage 2. I am, of course, fully aware that children may pick up these concepts away from home, from the mass media, and so on. But this could be handled appropriately, using the guidelines I have outlined for Stage 1 children.

Let us look more closely now at a *later* Stage 2 child, for it is within this age range that a child really begins to define religious concepts for himself. The entity most commonly shared by Western religions is that of God; it is important to keep in mind that the child's God may become an unconscious source of guidance and identification; his idea of God may become an integral part of his conscience. It is therefore exceedingly important to help introduce the child to a reasonable and easy-to-live-with God. The screaming evangelist, preoccupied with threats of hell, presents his listeners with the very antithesis of this kind of God.

I remind the reader of the fire-and-brimstone preacher only so that I might condemn him for his lack of insight and his profound stupidity. He instills into his congregation (which includes children) the picture of an angry, harsh, and punitive God, who is to be respected, if not feared. This concept of God represents a sick attitude and will be avoided by all parents with common sense and feeling for their children. The child who sees his God as punitive lives with unneeded fears and begins to generalize his fear of God to include other things. In other words, he begins to perceive the world as angry and harsh.

The concept of hell is also useless and harmful. I suspect that those evangelists who continue to peddle this asinine

idea are beyond redemption. Inculcation with such a negative entity as hell makes for intriguing books and horror
movies, but does little to promote a healthy attitude toward
religion.

Another cardinal rule follows this same line of thinking:
Never, in punishing a child, tell him that he is going to end
up in hell! This only distends his conscience with
unfounded fear that may return someday in the context of a
neurotic or psychotic disturbance. I am, of course, thinking
again of the patients I discussed in the chapter on the psychoses. Fear not: children tend to develop a conscience
without the use of such nonsense.

Another important general aspect of teaching religion to
the Stage 2 child is flexibility. Every child, as a result of (or
in spite of) his religious experience, will eventually develop
a philosophy of religion. If he personally has a major part
to play in assuming this philosophy, it will be more meaningful for him. The more structured and dogmatic his introduction to religion is, the less personal will be *his* investment in it.

The wise parent will allow organized religion to provide
only a superstructure or skeleton for childhood religious
guidance. This will involve a great deal of consideration by
the parent; he must mediate his own approach to religion
with common sense. His own best judgment must determine
which of the religious dicta are of greatest importance for
him and his child. In addition, as he presents these selected
ideas to his child, he must also allow the child to use *his*
judgment in accepting the ideas.

The use of force and punishment is utter foolishness; and
so he must present the material to his child with some
flexibility. The parent must be willing to limit his own use
of imagination in order to let his child imagine. I emphasize

again that one should avoid presenting overly structured details and dogma to children; let the child fill in some of the blanks with his own competent judgment. The Stage 2 child develops a powerful imagination of his own, as well as a good sense of reality, and should be allowed to design his own personal God with his own tools. Moreover, the parent, not the church or synagogue, should be in charge of his child's introduction to religion; this serves to avoid the creation of double messages as described in Chapter 2.

Example 2: Judy (age nine)

JUDY: Mom, today in Sunday School, Mrs. Goodfellow told us that Jesus was able to walk across the sea to join His disciples, who were waiting in a boat for Him. People really can't walk on water, can they, Mom?

MOM: Uh, no, Judy, people can't walk on water; only Jesus could.

JUDY: But I don't understand how He did that, Mom. How do you know that He really walked on water?

MOM: We know that, Judy, because it says so in the Bible, just as it says Jesus made a crippled man walk again.

JUDY: How did He do that, Mom? Was He a doctor too?

MOM: Of course not, Judy. He just did it; we know that because the Bible tells us that, and we must believe in the Bible.

JUDY: But, Mom, I don't understand how He did all those things. Neither does Mrs. Goodfellow.

MOM: Judy, you ask too many questions; maybe your father can answer them. Besides, you should not ask questions about the Bible. The Bible is the Holy Book and we must have faith in it and believe what it tells us.

Here you have witnessed a mother who feels highly threatened by her daughter's innocent and very reasonable questions. The mother responded to the questions with complacent rigidity, and a wall of misunderstanding was quickly erected. The mother's first mistake was her failure to perceive what Judy was "really" asking or, rather, stating. Judy was really saying (in her original question) that Mrs. Goodfellow tried to teach her a story that sounded preposterous. Judy was also stating that she did not believe the story, but knew better ("People really can't walk on water, can they, Mom?").

The little girl presented the question in an innocent fashion, but only for the sake of diplomacy. The mother, who has difficulty believing the Bible tale herself, refuses to answer the question. She merely attempts to silence the daughter with Biblical authority, Judy's persistence results in maternal frustration. So the mother reacts to her own bewilderment. Judy is told, essentially, to go away and to quit asking such sacrilegious questions.

Judy was not only stating something to her mother; she was testing her. The girl's powers of observation surpassed the mother's ability to cover up. Judy was able to sense that her mother was incapable of supporting Mrs. Goodfellow's tale. The result is serious and spills over into far more than religious questions. The girl became skeptical of her mother as well as of Mrs. Goodfellow.

Judy's mother handled the conversation poorly. Like many other "religious" people, she tended to lose her objectivity when it came to the matter of her own religion and the Bible. She seemed to put aside the fact that the Bible was written *by* and *of* people (to paraphrase Lincoln). She therefore ignored the possibility that she, or her daughter, could be justified in questioning Biblical writings.

It is educational to see how another mother would respond to the same question.

> JUDY: Mom, today in Sunday School Mrs. Goodfellow told us that Jesus was able to walk across the sea to join His disciples, who were in a boat waiting for Him. People really can't walk on water, can they?
>
> MOM: No, Judy, I don't think people can walk on water. The Bible tells us many tales that are sometimes difficult to believe. I don't think that I can tell you whether or not Jesus could walk on water or how He might have. It is more important, though, to learn what the Bible tells us about life, Judy. Some of the Bible tales may be difficult to believe, but may have a good moral. This is the important part—the moral of the story, not the story itself.

This mother was not only more sensible in her approach, but more honest. Her answer was natural, not devious. She was well aware that Judy was not "buying" the Bible tale and was able to respond to the girl's question with flexibility. Such a dialogue can be a mutually enriching experience for a mother and daughter because it is based in honesty.

Stage 3 Learning

There is little for the parent to do to guide his teen-ager in the development of healthy religious attitudes. It is more important to stress that the child coming out of Stage 2 has *already* developed a foundation of religious attitudes. If the parent challenges these attitudes, a fiasco may ensue. At that point the correct message is either "handle with care" or "hands off."

The Stage 3 child is often the most challenging, if only because he is more sophisticated than Stage 1 and 2 children and less naïve than Stage 3 children of the previous decade.

The case history (drawn from a newspaper) that opened this chapter (see page 114) represents *the* typical Stage 3 dilemma and must be approached carefully. A sample dialogue has already been demonstrated in my paraphrasing of the article.

The Stage 3 child is attempting to integrate his personality and establish a personal identity. This can be turbulent and painful for the whole family. As he begins the process of identity assumption, he must simultaneously emancipate himself from his parents. One "symptom" of this whole process is the tendency to question authority and at times to rebel. Within reason, this should be interpreted as healthy and normal. It is only logical that religion (which represents a kind of authority) becomes something for the child to rebel against.

By the time a child has reached his teens he has already outlined for himself some very definite attitudes about religious ritual, the Bible, and the sincerity of his parents' attitude toward religion. These attitudes are likely to change only at the discretion of the teen-ager, not the parents. The Stage 3 child finds delight in debating about religion with his parents; the result seems always to be a stalemate.

What often precipitates such debate is the parent's ambiguous religious attitude, which is easily perceived by the child. Typical is the Jewish parent who attends religious services twice a year but encourages his son to have a bar mitzvah and to attend services regularly. Another such paradox is the parent who never misses a day of worship, but who in daily life is an obvious bigot; the Stage 3 child is likely to refer to such a parent as a "chauvinist pig."

When dealing with Stage 3 children on religious matters, honesty is imperative: anything less will be obvious to these children. Above all, the parent must roll with some of the punches and not react to all of them. The mother in the newspaper example at the start of this chapter was reacting in a most arbitrary manner and, I suspect, was misguided by her probable fundamentalist religious attitudes. The parent should be willing to discuss religion with his teenager but should avoid inflicting beliefs on him; this only makes for open hostility directed by the parent to the child, who consequently feels guilt.

The parent who follows these simple guidelines has no guarantee that his children's religious attitudes will be healthy, but in most cases this should prove to be so. When it comes to religion, the wise parent will disprove the annoying cliché "You get out of something only what you put into it." If one "puts" too much emphasis on religion with a child, the child will benefit less.

The child with a healthy religious attitude enjoys identifying with and participating in his persuasion. He will actively question those aspects of his religion that do not fit into his personal scheme of life. He personally selects and rejects dicta according to his own value system. Such selectivity will not give rise to guilt feelings or atheism. He readily recognizes that his particular religion may have shortcomings. He does not react against religion but, rather, approaches it, examines it, accepts some of it, and discards the remainder. What he does not discard, he genuinely believes.

While he avoids atheism, he shies away from religious fanaticism. His healthy religious attitudes will spill over into his general outlook and augment a healthy adjustment to life.

CONDENSED PARENT'S GUIDE

Age	Stage 1

Stage 1

1
2
3
4
) Formal religious education is best avoided.

May begin to teach concrete, superficial religious rituals at home—for example, Christmas carols, candle lighting—etc.

5
6
Continue to avoid formal religious training and the teaching of abstract concepts. Defer answering abstract questions that might arise at this age. Avoid introduction to the Bible up to this point.

Stage 2

7
8
May now begin Sunday school teaching. Avoid dwelling on rules—for example, the Ten Commandments (except the few that are appropriate for this age). May introduce the concept of prayer by taking the child to religious services.

9
10
11
12
May now begin to introduce further the concept of God as well as other abstract subjects—but don't push it.

Encourage open communication on the various religious concepts (God, heaven, etc.). Be open and honest with the child and encourage him to question and to examine his religion.

It is especially important to set a good example here.

Stage 3

13
14
15
) Continue setting an example—that is, if you want your child to go to church . . . you go!
Avoid being dogmatic and authoritarian when it comes to religion.

16
17
18
) When in doubt, do nothing.
Always be honest—even when it hurts.
Don't push too hard—if you do, you are asking for a rebellion.

An Autobiographical Note

My childhood religious teachers provided the motivation for writing the preceding chapter. I began attending synagogue Sunday School at the age of four; the school was administered by people who had an incredible lack of insight with children.

At about the age of six I began seven years of Hebrew training. Learning Hebrew at the age of six can be equated with the experience of sitting on a park bench and counting the windows on the skyscraper across the street—backwards (from right to left). The net result of all this is that I can still read Hebrew, but still do not understand a word of it.

Hebrew school culminated in my bar mitzvah, traditionally symbolic of the achievement of manhood. This was anticlimactic for the precocious child that I was at the time. For me the bar mitzvah was the finale to seven years of extracurricular monotony.

It is perhaps only fair to let the reader know something of my personal beliefs.

My religious philosophy is neither unique nor profound. In general, I enjoy many of the Jewish customs and holi-

135

days, just as most Christians do theirs; I also enjoy the sense of Jewish identity that goes with my background. Though I gravitate toward belief in some kind of nebulous creational force, I find it difficult to imagine a God who listens to me or an afterlife that waits for me. On the other hand, for reasons apparent in Chapter 7, I tend to envy those who do have such genuine beliefs.

Selected Readings

Academy of Religion and Mental Health. *Research in religion and health.* New York: Fordham University Press, 1963.

Anderson, George Christian. *Your religion: neurotic or healthy?* Garden City: Doubleday, 1970.

Baken, David. *The duality of human existence; an essay on psychology and religion.* Chicago: Rand McNally, 1966.

Belgum, David Rudolph, ed. *Religion and medicine; essays on meaning, values, and health.* Ames: Iowa State University Press, 1967. (Iowa studies in religion and medicine.)

Biddle, W. E. *Integration of religion and psychiatry.* New York: Collier, 1962.

Clinebell, Howard J., Jr., ed. *Community mental health; the role of church and temple.* Nashville: Abingdon Press, 1970.

Fromm, Erich. *Psychoanalysis and religion.* New Haven: Yale University Press, 1950.

Gassert, Robert G., and Hall, Bernard H., *Psychiatry and religious faith.* New York: Viking Press, 1964.

Guirdham, Arthur. *Christ and Freud.* New York: Collier, 1962.

Hammes, John A. *Humanistic psychology; a Christian interpretation.* New York: Grune and Stratton, 1971.

James, William. *Varieties of religious experience.* New York: Mentor, 1958.

Klausner, Samuel Z. *Psychiatry and religion.* New York: Free Press, 1964.

Knight, James A. *A psychiatrist looks at religion and health.* Nashville: Abingdon Press, 1964.

Leuba, James Henry. *A psychological study of religion; its origin, function, and future.* New York: AMS Press, 1969.

Linn, Louis, and Schwarz, Leo W. *Psychiatry and religious experience.* New York: Random House, 1958.

Marti-Ibanez, Felix, ed. *Psychiatry and religion.* New York: MD Publications, 1956.

Maybaum, Ignaz. *Creation and guilt; a theological assessment of Freud's father-son conflict.* London: Vallentine, Mitchell, 1969.

Moore, Thomas V. *Heroic sanctity and insanity: an introduction to the spiritual life and mental hygiene.* New York: Grune and Stratton, 1959.

Moreno, Antonio. *Jung, gods and modern man.* Notre Dame: University of Notre Dame Press, 1970.

Mosbacher, Eric, trans. *Psychonanalysis and faith.* New York: Basic Books, 1963.

Mowrer, O. Hobart. *Crisis in psychiatry and religion.* New York: Insight Books, 1961.

National Association for Mental Health, 1967. *The role of religion in mental health.* Papers presented at a conference organized by the National Association for Mental Health in conjunction with the Institute of Religion and Medicine. London.

Northridge, William Lowell. *Psychiatry in pastoral practice.* 3d. ed. London: Epworth Press, 1968.

O'Doherty, Eamonn F., and McGrath, D. S. eds. *The priest and mental health.* New York: Alba House, 1963.

Pattison, E. Mansell, ed. *Clinical psychiatry and religion.* Boston: Little, Brown, 1969.

Philip, Howard Littleton. *Freud and religious belief.* London: Rockliff, 1956.

Sadler, William A., ed. *Personality and religion; the role of religion in personality development.* New York: Harper and Row, 1970.

Sheen, Fulton John. *Science, psychiatry, and religion.* New York: Dell Publishing Co., 1962.

Siegmund, Georg. *Belief in God and mental health.* New York: Desclee, 1965.

Stern, Karl. *The third revolution: a study of psychiatry and religion.* New York: Image, orig. published 1955.

Westberg, Granger E., and Draper, Edgar. *Community psychiatry and the clergyman.* Springfield, Ill.: C. C. Thomas, 1966.

Index

Index

DISCARDED

DISCARDED

DISCARDED